DIAGNOSIS
UNKNOWN

For George & Liz,

  Your feedback on reading the manuscript was very encouraging. Thanks for your interest in our story.

Love,

Randy Smith

Sept 11, 1997

DIAGNOSIS UNKNOWN

Our Journey to an Unconventional Cure

Randy Smith

HAMPTON ROADS
PUBLISHING COMPANY, INC.

for the evolving human spirit

For information write:

Hampton Roads Publishing Company, Inc.
134 Burgess Lane
Charlottesville, VA 22902

Or call: (804) 296-2772
FAX: (804) 296-5096
e-mail: hrpc@hrpub.com
Website: www.hrpub.com

If you are unable to order this book from your local
bookseller, you may order directly from the publisher.
Quantity discounts for organizations are available.
Call 1-800-766-8009, toll-free.

ISBN 1-57174-065-1

10 9 8 7 6 5 4 3 2 1

Printed on acid-free paper in Canada

This book is for Linda.

Acknowledgments

I am grateful to many people for their interest in and cooperation on this book. My wife, Linda, was not only the principal actor in our play, but its producer. Her willingness to allow me to describe the details of her many procedures is a demonstration of a lack of vanity unusual in so beautiful a woman. Our son, Noble, the real writer in the family, gave me valuable suggestions in organization and editing. Our son Shawn provided a great deal of moral support. My brother, Dr. Bart Smith, was my closest advisor throughout the entire experience. My mother, Mary Smith, typed the hand-written manuscript and made many suggestions. My father, Bob Smith, offered constant encouragement as he has done consistently my entire life. I am indebted to more than a dozen friends who read the manuscript and urged me to pursue publication. Ernie Martin, in particular, took an active interest in this project and led me to author Michael Schulman. Dr. Schulman provided an introduction to Al Zuckerman at Writer's House. Al took the book to his friends at Hampton Roads Publishing Company, Inc.

I am pleased to join the remarkable list of books published by the good folks at Hampton Roads. Thanks to Lizzie Crabtree, Violet Houser, Karen Whitehill, and especially, Frank DeMarco and, my editor, Bob Friedman for giving us a chance to see *Diagnosis Unknown* in print.

Table of Contents

Preamble

Linda Smith, a former Miss Seattle, once star of her own regional TV show, a highly regarded visual artist, performer in many community theater productions, devoted mother, community activist, antique collector, tennis player, bicycler, walker and hiker—a fit and very attractive forty-nine-year-old with no significant health problems on her resumé, woke up on her birthday with a dot on her eyelid. She believed it was a spider bite. Within two weeks the eye was swollen shut. Seven months later the eye was still grotesquely engorged. A year later she was a virtual invalid, a prisoner of her bedroom, her body racked with unexplainable symptoms. She was certain she was dying.

Chapter 1
The Bite

On her forty-ninth birthday, on November 1, 1992, Linda looked into the bathroom mirror and saw a small red dot on the flesh between the eyelid and brow of her left eye. She surveyed her birthday face. She was sensitive about her eyes and had always been dissatisfied with their appearance.

"My eyes are puffy," she would say. "Someday I'm going to get them fixed. I can hardly hold my eyelids up. There's just too much extra skin."

I had known Linda since I was twelve and she was eleven. We had been childhood sweethearts for awhile in junior high school and again for a brief interlude in college. She married someone else but I carried a torch and caught a nice rebound. She always looked good to me.

"Your eyes are fine," I would answer.

She stared at the dot. "Come look at this." I could see tiny red lines radiating from a center point.

"I think it's a bite," she said. Her statement was actually a question. After twenty-eight years of marriage I had developed enough sensitivity to read her oblique inflections.

"It'll be okay," I said. "It will go away."

"I think it's a bite," she continued. "When we walked around the park yesterday—remember when something flew into my eye? It's a spider bite."

"Spiders don't fly," I offered.

"It could have dropped down from a tree. There are lots of spiders in this house. We should get someone to spray."

"Poison would be worse than spiders," I argued. "You'll be okay. You have a strong body. Whatever it is will heal."

"Remember when Steve was bitten by the spider?" she asked.

"They weren't positive it was a spider," I replied quickly.

"Pretty sure. They were pretty sure. What else could it have been?" she wondered out loud, still staring in the mirror. "I want a doctor to see this."

Linda was convinced she had been bitten by a spider and was concerned because she had heard on more than one occasion that spider venom could desiccate the tissue leaving holes in the flesh. Our friend and former neighbor Steve, a physician, had presumably been bitten in his sleep by a brown recluse spider and nearly died, kept alive only by the massive intervention of his colleagues on the hospital medical staff. He had been shaken by the experience. We knew spider bites could be serious.

"It'll go away," I said again.

"You're not always right!" she told me. And it turned out I wasn't.

Within a few days the tissue around the dot began to redden and swell. As her eye began to close up, Linda experienced strange waves of unwellness. She believed it was spider venom coursing through her veins. She felt she was being poisoned. I was concerned about her reactions to this event but was confident the infection, or whatever it was, would disappear.

We were shocked when the eye continued to swell dramatically. In the corner of her left eye, close to the nose, a distended bag of fluid distorted her face. We stared at the eye, studied it with a magnifying glass, not knowing quite what to do or to say but, as always, assuming this ailment would run its course. She wanted to see a doctor immediately. We felt we knew how to enter the medical system. We had many friends and acquaintances who were physicians. An eye problem required an eye doctor. Even though we had recently moved to a new town and knew no doctors personally, it only took a week to get an appointment with an ophthalmologist—Dr. Elias. I had to take her. By that time the swelling had impaired her vision and she didn't feel safe driving a car.

Dr. Elias, the ophthalmologist, didn't know what it was.

"It might be a bite," he told her. "Or it could be an allergic reaction from a dust particle or animal matter of some type. I can't see any foreign objects in the eye."

Dr. Elias prescribed an antihistamine and cortisone cream. We went home to wait for the medicine to work. A week after this first visit to the doctor the eye was much worse. It hurt, it ached, it was scratchy. Each morning, it was filled with sticky stuff. I drove her back to the eye clinic. I sat in the waiting room and read several magazines.

Dr. Elias was apparently baffled.

"What did he say?" I asked as we walked to our car.

"He said he enjoys a good mystery!"

It was inconceivable to me that a highly trained eye specialist could not diagnose her condition. Why should it be such a mystery? I wondered what Elias would do with this mystery. How does a physician go about enjoying a good mystery? Does he sit in his den at night and quietly savor it?

What he did was the "handoff." He referred Linda to a local internist—Dr. Lewis. "An internist is a specialist at diagnosis," Dr. Elias told Linda. We knew that, of course. Our friend Steve was a board certified internist. She saw the second doctor a week later.

Dr. Lewis thought it was a bite. He told her to return in a week if it wasn't better and he would prescribe an antibiotic. Linda was upset because Dr. Lewis didn't even take a close look at the eye.

"He just glanced at it," she said in a confused tone. "He didn't even get close to me! Then he asked me if I'd had a pap smear lately. When I left he hollered at me as I was going down the hall, 'Have you signed up for a mammogram?' I don't want to go back to him."

"He's supposed to be good," I said, trying to be helpful.

"Who says?" she questioned.

We realized that we didn't know as much as we thought we did about how to enter the medical system. We had an eye problem so we picked an eye doctor. The eye doctor thought an internist, a diagnostic specialist, would have the right answer. That made good sense to us. But the internist didn't ask enough questions to come up with a diagnosis and was busy trying to promote pap smears and mammograms. Linda didn't really want any more X-rays. She wondered about radiation. Our new dentist had taken several X-rays during the summer. Linda had some concern that the swelling and redness was the result of X-rays. But finally, we decided that X-rays would also have to cause damage to the eyeball itself and Linda could see when she held her eye open.

We were concerned, but not worried. Everyone, even normally healthy people get sick once in awhile with a cold, flu, or other miscellaneous ailments. Experience told us that diseases are short-lived and self-limiting. We each had had years of experience with a quick visit to our family doctors for temperature, blood pressure, a glance down the throat, a peek in the ears, a hurried question, a friendly, reassuring smile, a pat on the back, and a slip of paper noting the silver bullet—the pill that would knock "it" out and the caveat to "take the entire prescription." If we were well acquainted with the physician we might also get samples, a handful of hermetically sealed drugs left by the pharmaceutical salesman for the doctor to "try out." "These new drugs are very effective," the salesman would say to the doctor. "These are supposed to be good," the doctor would tell us.

Such was our medical experience—an occasional visit for a cold, flu, skin ailment, mammogram, pap smear, or physical exam. We believed, as we were told that we had the greatest medical system in the world. We had no chronic ailments and were not on continuing medication. Our hearts were strong; we were not overweight. We thought we were healthy.

We had no way of knowing it at that time but the spider bite, the swollen eye, was to lead us into the most bizarre adventure of our lives. We were embarking on a medical mystery tour—Dr. Elias knew a good mystery when he saw one—which would take us through the stations of conventional medicine and into the unfamiliar and curious world of alternative medical therapies. We would become explorers and adventurers, experimenting with a long list of unconventional, even illegal, therapies. We would be reeducated in the subjects of health and wellness. In the end, the spider bite would transform us both.

In the interim after Linda's appointments with the ophthalmologist and internist, while we were considering what to do next, we could not possibly have conjured the reality of our next two years. If someone had told me then that my wife would be bedridden for months at a time and I would have to take over all of the household responsibilities and become a full-time nurse, I would have scoffed. If we had been told Linda's eye would be swollen for a full year, that most of her hair would fall out, that her fingers would curl up from arthritis, that every muscle and joint would ache, that her nose would fill with scabs, that she wouldn't have enough strength to walk across the living room, and that she would have more than 150 appointments with doctors, therapists, and practitioners, we would have said it was a fantasy. If someone had tried to tell us that even a full year later, Linda would be chronically ill and we would still be searching for a diagnosis, we would have been incredulous.

If someone had told us our answers would finally come from a man who used a computer and copper probes to diagnose her ailments precisely and tell her what to do to get well, we would have told them they were nuts. And, if someone had told us we would, in the future, willingly forego medical insurance and get our medical treatment from radiations that are broadcast like radio signals through the atmosphere, we would have expected to be considered candidates for an asylum.

Of course, no one was able to tell us anything. We had to learn it all for ourselves.

Chapter 2
Our Medical History

With every previous ailment we had experienced, the doctor had told us what was wrong and gave us a pill. Something had bitten Linda on the eye. We needed to find the expert who could diagnose the problem and prescribe medication that would counteract the poison.

We naturally turned to the Yellow Pages. Dr. Silvers was the eye, ear, nose, and throat (ENT) specialist in town. It seemed a logical next step. We decided to try Dr. Silvers. We were committed to finding a solution.

In Dr. Silvers' office we were required, of course, to complete a questionnaire detailing our medical history. Since he kept us waiting for awhile, I had time to reflect on my family's medical saga.

For people my age (fifty-two), there has always been a pharmaceutical solution for every problem. My generation was the first not to worry about lock jaw or polio. From the first day of school in 1948, we were immunized with the wonder drugs being produced by our scientists. Like puppies, we got our shots from first grade through military induction.

There was a pervasive belief that every ailment had a pharmaceutical remedy. There was a silver bullet, or there soon would be, for every disease. Cancer was a problem. They were having trouble with that one, as well as heart disease and some of the unusual stuff like multiple sclerosis. But it was only a matter of time until our medical scientists would discover a drug that would solve the problem—just as our scientists had discovered how to make the bomb that won the war.

In the modern medical war, the viral and bacterial invaders who were attempting to control the landscape of our bodies would, in the end, be repelled and defeated by the special weapons now being developed in our research laboratories. We were an invincible country and no invader, foreign, viral, or bacterial could long battle the brainpower and inventive genius of our great nation.

Our drug stores became a wonderland of salves, ointments, tablets, and capsules, each promising a quick solution but carrying a recommendation that if symptoms persisted we see our physician. We had to see the physician to get the good stuff. We all knew that one needed a prescription for the more potent drugs—the antibiotics, strong painkillers, and relaxants. The physician provided a point of control to make sure we used the drugs properly and not indiscriminately. He would prescribe the correct amount to make us well and, at the same time, insure that we did not take so much as to make the drug ineffective for us in the future.

Over the years the varieties of drugs multiplied so rapidly that we couldn't keep them straight. We wondered if the doctor could. The pharmacists seemed to know more about the pills than the doctor—especially the side effects. We heard that there was some danger in taking too many antibiotics, that germs could develop immunity to specific drugs. We presumed that was the reason that new antibiotics were always coming on line. We had confidence that our doctors would always find a solution to our problems. After all, they had destroyed tetanus, polio, and smallpox; cholera and syphilis and gonorrhea; and bubonic plague and leprosy. They were on a roll and we had very little to worry about—medically speaking. We did what they told us to do.

When I was a kid our family doctor was Dr. Bond. After Linda and I were married he took care of us for ten years until we moved to another city. Dr. Bond was the epitome of the family doctor. He was always available, though we were accustomed to waiting at least an hour past the appointment time. He was a surgeon who could remove your hemorrhoids or deliver your baby. He started early at the hospital, saw patients in his office all day, and ended up back at the hospital. His office was packed with loyal and devoted patients. When he saw his own family, I do not know. He was warm and funny and reassuring. Dr. Bond was our unquestioned medical authority. He was on a pedestal. He didn't ask to be there; we placed him there. It was obvious he wasn't in it for the money, although he certainly made plenty. He didn't have time to use his country club membership. He was rarely able to sail his small boat. He (or at least Mrs. Bond) lived in a very nice but modest home. We assumed he was dedicated to helping people get well.

We had had another family doctor before Dr. Bond moved to town. We switched to Dr. Bond because the other doctor killed himself. I remember that I was very disturbed when our doctor committed suicide. I couldn't understand why a physician, who I recognized as being among the most admired professions in the community, would take his own life. My mother explained that doctors were under a lot of pressure because sometimes they weren't able to help people. This was the first indication I had ever had that doctors might be fallible.

Linda and I married the last year I was in the Air Force, and we moved to Ft. Walton Beach, Florida. She became pregnant and I was thrilled because we had free medical care. She was not thrilled because the base hospital did not provide the kind of personalized service she desired. "I never know which one will be looking at me," she complained throughout her pregnancy. The "which ones" were the trio of doctors assigned to obstetrics at the Eglin AFB Hospital and who were named (I am not making this up!) Dr. Box, Dr. Cox, and Dr. Hyman. As Linda's labor dragged on throughout a long day, we thought it would be Box, then Cox, then Hyman who would deliver our baby as the shifts came and went. Finally, our son was delivered by a doctor she had never seen before and whose name we do not know. And, based on my experience in the waiting room, I am still relieved that he was safely delivered at all. Another man and I were waiting together when the unknown doctor came out to tell my waiting-room partner that he had a son. The doc was wearing his surgical smock and was covered in blood. "You've got a nice boy," he said to the young sergeant. "He had a hard time getting out. I had to put the forceps on him and pull. Thought I was going to pull his head off! Ha! Ha!"

"Get me out of here," she said as soon as the infant was cradled in her arms. The next day we left with a bill for $6.00 and some strange memories.

We were discharged and returned home to Everett, Washington and the care of Dr. Bond. For the next ten years he helped us forget our doubts about doctors raised by Box, Cox, and Hyman. But, then, as a family we had no unusual problems.

It was during this period of the 1970s that, through a strange combination of circumstances, we stopped smoking and drinking and became vegetarians. Truth to tell, Linda had never smoked, used alcohol, or even drank coffee. Her favorite foods had always been things like steamed broccoli or cauliflower. She would eat the leftover veggies. We did not become vegetarians specifically for health reasons, although we believed it would be a secondary benefit. We took up vegetarianism because it was part of a yoga practice we adopted. Eating vegetarian does not automatically guarantee a healthy diet. It is still probable that a lacto-vegetarian, such as we were, could eat too much dairy, too much sugar, and, surprisingly, too much protein.

A vegetarian in the corporate insurance world in the 1970s was an oddity and even a curiosity. As far as I know, at the Seattle offices of Safeco Insurance, a company of several thousand well-groomed employees, I was the only employee who confessed to being a vegetarian. I ate in the cafeteria with everyone else. At business lunches and banquets, I became adept at seeking out the headwaiter and arranging a fruit plate.

I took an aggressive position if attacked for my eating habits, quickly pointing out to the attacker that meat, especially beef, was loaded with uric acid. "Do you know what uric acid is?" I would ask, setting my little trap. "It's piss," I would state with a half smile on my face. "You're eating piss soaked meat." No one wanted to hear this kind of thing, and I was mostly left alone to die a slow death by protein starvation.

In 1978 we bought into an insurance agency and our family of four—Linda, me, and our sons Shawn and Noble—moved to Yakima, Washington, a city existing because of an irrigated valley that produces apples, pears, cherries, mint, hops, peaches, corn, and a variety of other crops. In this fruit and vegetable bowl we were, as far as I know, one of the few vegetarian couples, more curious than we had been on Puget Sound. Yakimans love their meat as evidenced by every restaurant menu. It was assumed we were health nuts—which we weren't. In Yakima we were never able to connect with a family doctor. Most were "not taking new patients," which I guessed meant they were making enough money. Yakima, in addition to being a major fruit and vegetable center, was a regional medical center with two grand hospitals and a smaller osteopathic hospital. There were many highly-regarded board certified specialists in the area but few family practitioners which, according to an occasional medical article that caught my eye, was an alarming trend in medicine. No one wanted to be Dr. Bond anymore. Too much work and not enough reward.

Living in Yakima, in spite of its vast medical resources, caused me to have some passing environmental health concerns. In the spring the air would be thick with petroleum smoke as the farmers whose orchards surrounded the city smudged for heat, in their fight to keep the temperatures above freezing, losing sleep to save the buds. During this annual battle, one would wake to the distant sound of wind machines, huge propellers on a pole, and the sticky scent of burning oil. Later, and throughout the summer, tractor-driven spray rigs raised clouds of pesticides and insecticides. Orchard properties would be posted with signs in two languages, "Peligro/Danger." In winter, inversions would lid our basin valley, holding in the smoke from wood fueled fireplaces, creating a gray cast over this normally sunny place, and on bad days it would induce fog. As the years passed and the population grew, these inversions which held the bad air over us seemed to last most of the winter.

In the spring of 1980, Mt. St. Helens blew up and a whole community, for a few minutes at least, thought it would suffocate on sulfurous fumes. But the volcanic eruption was not hazardous to health after the dust settled. Our water tasted funny, though. We had city water, which was piped in from the Cascades Mountains, then treated, we presumed, with chlorine and other chemicals. We installed a reverse osmosis water purifier but did not refuse to drink water at restaurants or water fountains as we made our way around town.

On the other side of town, in an area too poor to be a candidate for the aggressive annexation policies of city bureaucrats, poor people, mostly Mexicans, lived in tiny frame houses with plastic wrap for storm windows. These residents drank well water often contaminated with chemicals or gasoline from the many old and leaking underground tanks. There was concern about the aquifer and its pollution from a combination of overuse and years—nearly a century—of agricultural spraying of long-forgotten poisons like DDT (or other forbidden chemicals).

On the west side of Yakima, where we lived, people didn't like to think about the effects of our community's economic activity on our corporate health. Our newspaper, even though it was owned by out-of-town interests and enjoyed a monopoly on print journalism, did nothing to explore the possible dangers of the chemistry of agriculture. In the mid-1980s when the National Resources Defense Council got "60 Minutes" to blow the whistle on Alar as a potential carcinogen used on apples, the grumpy old men who controlled the fruit became defensive and convinced an apple-dependent community to grumble as well about that goddamn Ed Bradley and Meryl Streep, who quickly replaced Jane Fonda as the actress you'd most like to slap silly.

"Bad science," cried the fruitmen. "We've been damaged," briefed their lawyers. Our doctors, as I remember, were silent. But it was a chemical. It was used on the fruit and after the flap they quit using it, as they had quit using DDT and a long list of other certifiably dangerous poisons. In a community like Yakima there was no pressure for any ombudsman, journalist or otherwise, to investigate the health of the local environment. The initials EPA were as odious in Yakima as IRS.

From my own tours of the world of insurance claims, I was aware of huge underground gasoline leaks which contaminated wells; ammonia leaks in fruit warehouses that hospitalized workers; fumes emanating from service stations that gave people headaches; agricultural over-sprays that killed neighboring crops and beekeeper's bees; poisonous runoff from orchards that left dead fish floating in commercial fish ponds; and dust and flies from feedlots that antagonized neighbors. I was aware of a road in an agricultural area of Yakima on which resided as many as a dozen farmers who had experienced prostate cancer in a short period of time. And on every orchard I ever visited, I would find an oily spot of ground where the sprayers had been washed out for decades, leaving petrochemical molecules to soak into the earth.

I surely didn't get on my soap box either but over the years I began to recognize, as did many Americans, that we were living in a chemical soup. The problem seemed so vast as to defy solutions. My evidence was not scientific; I was reduced to anecdote. Anecdotally, I decided there might be healthier places to live than in the seemingly healthful and athletically-oriented Yakima Valley. I wasn't the public health officer. and had no science to offer my friends and associates. I was just an insurance peddler. But this is the great thing about anecdotal information. One can use it as one pleases for one's own use.

To the east of us was the Hanford Nuclear Reservation and the Tri-Cities, where our business had a branch office. A few years earlier, Linda and I had debated moving to the Tri-Cities to manage that office but declined because of the geological bleakness of the area and a vague concern about radiation. Subsequent to our decision were the revelations of the early 1990s that radioactive material had been released on several occasions and probably did cause the excessive incidence of cancer to those unfortunate enough to be downwind. These revelations seemingly did not dissuade anyone else from moving to the Tri-Cities, as the area experienced a new boom when the federal government began to pour millions, perhaps billions, into Hanford to clean up the mess.

Back in Yakima the majority of citizens were relieved that their fertile valley, irrigated by a massive system of canals and water from the beautiful snow-covered Cascades to the west, did not face the dangers posed by the nuclear reactors ninety miles east. Out of sight; out of mind. Our friends weren't entirely out of touch. They were rearranging their diets in the 1980s to reduce their red meat consumption and substituting local wines for harder liquors. The YMCA had an active program to rehabilitate the men and a couple of women who had had their chests unzipped by the specialists from the Heart Center. The hospitals provided regular lectures on a variety of health issues but they emphasized women's health in particular. Mammograms were promoted on local television, and there was a whole clinic full of radiologists available to interpret the pictures.

The two hospitals wavered between cooperation and competition and relentlessly expanded their physical plants, raising money through the offices of full-time development executives, fund raisers who took rich people to lunch and organized golf tournaments, auctions, and fashion shows. They had a nose for the cash and knew which buttons to push to release it to their respective medical collectives.

We were among the few who admitted going to a chiropractor. It was clear that others were going too, as the number of chiropractic offices was growing. Some chiropractors even built big new offices. One even played golf at the club, although it was understood that members of the American Medical Association were enjoined from associating with him—even for a game of golf. On the outskirts of the city was the mysterious Total Health Foundation, which was operated by some Seventh Day Adventist physicians who had a family practice downtown. During fifteen years in Yakima, I never met or heard of anyone who had spent a session at Total Health Foundation which, it was alleged, put people on a vegetarian diet and made them walk every day to lower blood pressure, reduce cholesterol, and break cigarette habits. In the late 1980s a naturopathic doctor moved to town and set up an office in a small frame house behind the medical center. I never heard of anyone who went there either. No one knew what naturopathic meant, but it was rumored the first visit cost $300 and was not covered by most medical plans.

Mainstream medicine dominated the health scene in Yakima which, because of its geographical location, was considered a regional medical center. The doctors and hospitals drew patients from a large rural area. It was the last stop before Seattle. Seattle, of course, was on the "A" list of medical destinations with a lineup of renowned hospitals—University, Swedish, Virginia Mason, Hutchinson Cancer Center, and the much-supported Children's Orthopedic Hospital.

Save for chiropractic and the lonely naturopath there were no alternatives to hospital-based medicine. Traditional health care owned a monopoly supported by lack of information on other options and by a control of the insurance mechanism. We had one system of medicine. "If it's paid for, I will go there," was the prevailing attitude. There was no other.

Of course, as a community we were vaguely aware that in other countries the medical systems were slightly different, though certainly not as good. When Nixon went to China and an accompanying journalist got acupuncture in a Chinese hospital, the reporter gave acupuncture a publicity boost and a positive connotation. But, then, most people thought of acupuncture as a pain reliever. England and Canada had socialized medicine, which, by definition, is very bad. We knew little about medical practice in Germany or France. Possibly Americans were under the impression that all the brilliant Germans had migrated to the U.S. after World War II. It was curious that Americans who will spend hours investigating the relative merits of automobiles and who would, as a group, acknowledge the superiority of Mercedes and BMWs, would not wonder what the Germans were doing in medicine. But we had more important things to worry about—such as cars and football—so we delegated our medical problems to our doctors and hospitals and drug companies.

Our personal experiences with foreign medicine had not been all that satisfactory. In 1989 Linda and I traveled to Paris to experience the bicentennial of the French Revolution. Shortly after we arrived, Linda became quite ill with flu-like symptoms. In Paris, if you are an American and you get sick, you pick up the phone and call "S.O.S. Medicins." In less than forty-five minutes, Dr. Pierre Fournier responded to our call appearing at our hotel with a brown leather bag. He took temperature and blood pressure, looked in the throat and ears, wrote a prescription, and collected his fee in cash. We couldn't understand exactly what Linda had but thought he said "flu" or "virus." I took the antibiotic prescription down to the pharmacy on the corner. Two days later she was worse and wanting to go to a hospital. I called S.O.S. Medicins again. In forty minutes Dr. Stephane Aszerman appeared with his brown leather bag, did his exam, told us to stop the antibiotic and take the medicines he prescribed. He seemed to be saying that his colleague Dr. Fournier, Diplome de Medicine Tropical, had slightly misdiagnosed the ailment and that he, Aszerman, Laureate de la Faculte de Medicin de Paris, was on the right track. I handed him his cash and took the prescription note, which I still have but cannot read, to my friendly pharmacist. A few days later Linda seemed to be mending. She desperately wanted to see the Louvre, and I managed to get her there for a whirlwind tour, leaving quickly when she threatened to vomit into a sarcophagus.

In New Delhi two years previously our son, Noble, came down with a severe chest cold and stomach cramps. We saw an Indian doctor who prescribed Benzedryl and Magnesium Tri-Silicate with Belladonna, two medicines unknown to us. He told me I could get them filled at the hospital around the corner. I found the Kapur Memorial Hospital. A small, elderly security guard in brown trousers and a khaki sweater stepped forward to assist me. "Chemist?" I asked. He pointed his nightstick toward the main entrance. Right inside the door was a large sign which said "Drug Store" in English and Hindi. An old man in a suit sitting at a small counter appeared to be the pharmacist. Four assistants stood next to him. I pushed the prescription across the counter to the first assistant. He very quickly found a bottle of Benzedryl and wrote up a receipt. He studied the balance of the prescription and passed it to the next assistant. It moved down the line of assistants and ultimately ended up in the hands of the old guy who studied it a very long time then delivered it back to me through the human chain.

"Not legeebool," I thought the assistant said as he pushed it through the opening in the glass. I bent and twisted my ear to the opening.

"What?" I asked.

"Not availeebool," I thought he said the second time. The old man began to speak to me. I believe he was trying to explain why he couldn't fill it. I understood him to say that I should go to a chemist in the Chani Market. I paid fifty cents for the cough medicine, which raised some questions in my mind about price gouging in the U.S.A.

I returned to the doctor's office, and he instructed his assistant to take me to the chemist. A fat young man dressed in white led me to his motor scooter. I climbed on the back of the blue two-wheeler holding my paper sack of Benzedryl in one hand and the fat man in the other. When we arrived, the chemist shop was busy. After studying the prescription for a long time the chemist handed it back.

"Not legible," he said.

We returned on the scooter and I had the doctor print the prescription. The doctor's assistant told me he would get it filled. I gave him fifty rupees and he left me to sit alone. An hour later he returned and handed me the fifty rupees and the prescription.

"Not available," he said.

From our experience, foreign medicine left much to be desired.

The year before the India trip, I had injured my knee playing tennis. I visited a busy and respected orthopedic surgeon I didn't know personally but who actually was almost a neighbor. He lived on the next street over. He X-rayed my knee and pulled it and twisted it a couple of times and quickly told me I had arthritis and there wasn't much he could do. "I can scrape it," he said, "But, I'll just have to do it again every couple of years. You may have to live with it." I was out the door with a bill for $150 as baffled by his diagnosis as he was by my arthritis. One of my neighbors had arthritis, and I knew she had an artificial ankle invented by a doctor in Seattle. The local doctors hadn't helped her much but the new ankle seemed to work. She gave me his name, St. Norton Fields III, M.D., who apparently was also highly regarded by the

Catholic Church. It occurred to me that at the rate the medical profession was progressing, he would not be the last M.D. to achieve sainthood in his lifetime. I made an appointment and visited his well-organized office, located near Swedish Hospital. He looked at my X-rays, asked me a lot of questions, manipulated my knee and sold me some arthroscopic surgery. I'd known lots of people who had their knees "scoped." It was routine. Being pretty sure it was a cartilage tear, I had expected surgery. "Torn meniscus," said my saint doctor. "No problem. You'll be jogging and playing tennis in six weeks." We set a date. I got a second opinion from his partner down the hall, who looked at the pictures and signed off on the insurance forms.

Swedish Hospital was a well-oiled machine. They rolled me into an operating room. The anesthesiologist briefed me, gave me a shot, talked me into a spinal block, and got me to sign some forms. He gave me a shot. My legs went dead. Dr. Fields came in and said "Hi, let's get to work." He turned on a black-and-white TV. I felt something pushing hard on my leg, then again and again. On the screen, I could see a Pac Man type thing chomping away on some white stuff. "The cartilage is torn, all right," said St. Doctor. I began to see some white threads on the screen. "Oh, oh," said the doc, "There is some arthritis here."

His fee, as best I remember was about $1200. The anesthesiologist was about $400. The total bill nearly $3000. I was walking in a week and the knee still works for walking, golfing, hiking, and biking, but not for jogging or tennis.

Insurance covered most of this operation, as it did with office calls, some dental bills, and even twenty chiropractic visits per year. Doctor's offices seemed obsessed with insurance, as it was the first thing they asked you about when you signed into the waiting room. My customers were increasingly complaining about medical insurance and its rising cost. Employers looked for ways to cut costs while insurance companies looked for ways to reduce coverage. Insurance totally ignored the other healing arts of acupuncture, naturopathy, massage, and the like. The medical examiners of the insurance companies were M.D.s. It was a closed system. No one else need apply.

From my viewpoint, the doctor business looked pretty good. I didn't personally know of any physicians in Yakima who worked as hard as Dr. Bond, although I'm sure there were some. They seemed, as a group, upwardly mobile, driving fine cars, moving up in the real estate market, taking posh vacations often at the expense of pharmaceutical companies. There were a few doctors who volunteered a month in the third world, which was commendable, and others who did their bit in the community. The physicians' wives provided the backbone of many of the arts and social service organizations in our city. I knew for a fact that a number of specialists had incomes in excess of $500,000 per year and that $300,000 wasn't unusual. They were doing quite well, thank you, in spite of the high insurance premiums we collected from them.

In 1988, our family was subjected to an infinitely more complicated medical experience than arthroscopic surgery. Our son Shawn, who was on active duty with the United States Air Force and due to get out, was diagnosed during his discharge physical as having a cyst on his heart. The Air Force recommended immediate surgery. The surgery was no simple matter. A thoracic surgeon would open his back in a large arcing incision, spread the ribs, and delicately excise the cyst which was wrapped entirely around one side of the heart. Shawn was scared silly.

We had him come home to get a second opinion from Dr. Mason, a Yakima Internist, who specialized in diseases of the chest. He reviewed the file and opined that surgery might not be necessary. He told us that this kind of cyst was usually not cancerous, and might never get bigger. He could check in a year and decide on surgery then. This information was heartening but problematic when we began to consider the financial ramifications. If he had the surgery now, the military would pay for it since Shawn was still on active duty. If he opted not to undergo the knife, the cyst would be a preexisting condition on whatever medical insurance policy he might obtain in the future and, thus, this surgery—estimated civilian cost of $25,000 assuming no complications and a minimum hospital stay—would be, as they say, "not covered." Dr. Mason, a cautious man, felt we needed a third opinion, and he sent the pictures to the Thoracic Surgery Department of University of Washington Medical School. Their emphatic advice was to cut. Dr. Mason wavered slightly and suggested that surgery might be a better course than worrying about a cyst grasping one's heart year after year.

Shawn understood the options. It was his call. We didn't know what caused the cyst. If we had, it might have helped. Was it cancerous? A biopsy wouldn't tell anything. It was like poking a needle into a haystack unless the whole thing was consumed with cancer cells. Was there any other way to get rid of it? Diet, prayer, psychic surgery? We had no answers and few options. Shawn scheduled an operation. The surgeon did a wonderful job of excising the cyst and suturing the incision. But along with the cyst they removed his thymus gland. We didn't even know he had a thymus gland.

In the past, as a people, we had so completely delegated the care of our bodies to the medical establishment that we knew very little about how they worked. Most of us knew the basics. Eating, breathing, exercising, eliminating. But on the whole, we knew very little about what our organs actually did and, more importantly, how our bodies worked to fight infections and maintain health. The thymus gland is a good example. Consider this quote from *World Medicine: The East West Guide to Healing Your Body* by Tom Monte.

"Western scientists have only recently begun to appreciate the thymus. Only a few decades ago, doctors believed it was a useless organ, especially in adulthood, because it usually begins to shrink after puberty. Today, scientists know that the thymus gland is essential to a healthy immune system. Located in the upper part of the chest just below the breastbone, the thymus is slightly smaller than a fist, with two lobes that are packed with tiny immune cells called lymphocytes. The function of the thymus is to produce lymphocytes and to train them to distinguish. . .one's own cells from diseased cells. The thymus is essential to healthy immune function."

Apparently the army surgeon who ripped off Shawn's thymus didn't appreciate that it had any significance.

In 1991, our son Noble reported that his orthodontist had recommended surgery which would require his palate to be split so that it could then be spread apart, widening the upper jaw by 30 percent, allowing his teeth to be straightened and his bite to align properly. (Treated before puberty, this condition is reportedly simple to correct. For an adult it is a nightmare. Our family dentist had never recommended orthodontia for Noble. Failure to correct the problem would result in the loss of all his teeth by age thirty because they were improperly aligned, causing orthodontic trauma. The surgery was an uninsured procedure with a total cost, including orthodontics, of around $10,000. We told him to go ahead.

The surgery was painfully uncomfortable. An incision was made in the palate. An appliance with a screw mechanism was inserted against the palate, and his morning duty was to arise and turn that screw a partial revolution causing the two front teeth to move apart a millimeter at a time. The front teeth separated to a point where he could insert a pencil between them. This agony was fed by a liquid diet for nearly eight months and soft foods for another eight months. A high price for a beautiful smile.

In May of 1992 we sold our business, retired, and moved from Yakima, Washington, to Ashland, Oregon. A few months before we moved, a Yakima endodontist, Dr. Skip Vernon, had treated Linda for infection in two adjacent molars on the upper left side of her jaw which he had root-canaled in the summer of 1990. The teeth continued to bother her and had abscessed through the gum. Dr. Vernon believed she might be having a "rare" allergic reaction to the material used in the root canals. He operated on the abscess and redid the root canals. To fight the infection he gave her a course of Amoxicillin, followed by a larger course of Tetracycline,* another antibiotic. The gum seemed to improve.

Shortly after we arrived in Ashland, Linda's gum and jaw flared up. Her cheekbone began to hurt. Linda called Dr. Vernon's office in Yakima and, by phone, he prescribed another course of Amoxicillin. She saw an oral surgeon and an endodontist in Medford, Oregon. They both recommended pulling the tooth because of a visible sore on the gum which was evidence to them of abscess. Linda's local dentist in Ashland, felt he could save the tooth. He believed she was having TMJ (Temporomandibular Joint Syndrome) problems and that an improper bite was putting pressure on the root-canaled teeth causing pain in the jaw.

In August she caught a bad chest cold and developed a dry cough. I took her to a friend of ours who was a physician's assistant in a family medical clinic. The doctors there gave her a complete physical with blood work and an EKG and tested her for both menopause and pregnancy. Everything tested normal. They said she was not menopausal or pregnant. They gave her a cough syrup and Erythromycin, still another antibiotic.

During August her cheekbone and jaw continued to ache. The physician's assistant recommended she have the tooth pulled. But Linda was concerned about losing permanent teeth. In great pain, she finally decided to have the tooth pulled and convinced her dentist to extract it. When he pulled the molar from the upper left side of her jaw, he could see that it was, in fact, still abscessed. This abscess did not show up on the X-rays.

In October, we car tripped with my parents through the Southwest. In Santa Fe, Linda suddenly announced she wanted to go to the emergency room. She was having difficulty breathing, her heart was racing. She feared she might be having a heart attack. At St. Vincent's Hospital the physician took chest X-rays, administered an EKG, and did blood work, nearly the same program she had in August. Her white cell count was elevated, and the doctor gave her a chest inhaler and another course of Amoxicillen.

We returned home. Then, in November, the spider bite.

To sum up this medical history, our nuclear family had given up some knee cartilage, a half pound of hemorrhoids (details politely omitted), a big cyst with thymus, had submitted to a palate spreading, and been operated on for dental abscess. We had experienced no broken bones and only minor cuts and sprains. As a group, we had experienced assorted childhood and self-limiting infectious diseases. We had no illnesses that prevented our accomplishment of normal duties for periods of longer than two weeks. We had no known allergies; no chronic ailments of any kind. We had regular medical checkups and were deemed healthy by both physicians and life insurance companies. We visited our dentist regularly for cleaning and checkups. We flossed. Illness, if it came, was temporary. If we couldn't whip it with bed rest and juice, we'd go for a pill, certain of a knockout punch. We did not dwell on illness. It was not a preoccupation. We expected to feel well. Frankly, we were not concerned about chronic illness or serious disease.

Chapter 3
We're Going to the Doctor

Dr. Silvers reviewed our medical history briefly and asked no questions. Then, he examined the eye. He wondered if the sinuses were involved. He gave Linda a prescription for Lorabid and sent us up to the Radiology Department of the Ashland Community Hospital for full sinus X-rays. Linda was hopeful that the new drug would help, although she was apprehensive about more x-rays to her face. The radiology personnel were very courteous, and from behind their lead shield, assured her there was no danger from X-rays. She began taking Lorabid.

The spider bite, so-called, had occurred on the first day of November. Linda started Lorabid on December 11. Two days later on a Sunday night I was settling into my chair to watch "60 Minutes." Linda came out of the bathroom.

"Call an ambulance," she ordered.

"What?"

"I'm going to pass out! Please call an ambulance. Call it now."

I looked at her carefully. Other than the swollen eye she looked fine. I didn't believe she would pass out. I didn't want to call an ambulance.

"Look," I said, getting up and holding her hand, "sit for a minute. You'll feel better."

"No, I won't," she said angrily. "I think I'm dying. Call the ambulance. I need to go to the hospital."

I decided not to argue. But I did negotiate.

"It will take the ambulance ten to fifteen minutes to get here. The hospital is only five minutes away. I'll help you to the car and we'll be there in five minutes."

"All right," said Linda. "Please; let's go."

We live on a very steep hill. Our house, built in 1912, has no garage or driveway. The street is very narrow, almost an alley and in the winter we park at the bottom of the hill.

"Hold my arm," I said as we walked down the hill. I helped her into the car and made a U-turn to get going in the direction of the hospital.

"I'm fading," she said. "I think I'm dying. I think I'm going to die tonight."

"No, you're not. You're not dying." But I could tell she really believed it was true.

I drove faster. It took less than five minutes to reach the hospital. We pulled into the parking lot and walked into the emergency room. There was another couple at the desk. Linda, who is normally too polite, interrupted their discussion.

"I'm not doing well. I need someone to look at me right now."

The nurse glanced at her.

"We'll be with you in a second," she told Linda, indicating she should take a seat.

"No," said Linda sharply. "I need help now."

"What's wrong?" asked the nurse with some hostility.

"I was bitten by a spider." She removed her dark glasses and displayed her hugely swollen left eye. The nurse still wouldn't react. Linda persisted until they took her into the small emergency room.

She lay on her back on the ER bed with the curtain pulled around for privacy. I was starting to become familiar with emergency rooms, the chemically-induced antiseptic smell, the glaring lights. An old man was coughing on the other side of the room.

"I love you," she said holding my hand tightly. "We've had a pretty nice life, don't you think?"

This is all very melodramatic, I thought. I was certain in my own mind that she wasn't dying. I was beginning to think she was having some kind of reaction to the new antibiotic—Lorabid.

"I love you, too," I said with great sincerity.

"Make sure you look after the kids," she said seriously. It was obvious that Linda was playing out a death scene in her own mind.

"The kids are grownups," I replied.

"But they still need you." Her eyes were full of tears. "Do you think you'll get married again?" she asked very seriously.

At that moment I wasn't thinking about marriage. At that moment a powerful peristaltic wave was sweeping through my bowel. I wanted to rush from her bedside and find the rest room which I knew must exist just outside the curtained bed. I fought the wave determined to show some sensitivity to my dying spouse. It was ludicrous to think that she was dying. On the other hand, I didn't want my conscience to be burdened by the memory that I had been taking a crap while she passed away.

"Are you okay?" she wondered." "Your face looks pale. You're sweating."

"I'm just worried. That's all. Worried about you." The crisis, for me at least, had passed.

The doctor finally arrived. He was on call to handle emergencies. His name was Dr. Burnett and he was much younger than we were. He had a wonderful bedside manner–quiet, sympathetic, and concerned. He was an excellent listener. I was pleased that he zeroed in on the antibiotic. "It's new and it's strong," he told us.

Linda was suffering from heart palpitations, dizziness, and blurred vision. She was having trouble getting her breath. Dr. Burnett was thorough. He sent her out for chest X-rays, EKG, and blood test, the same regimen she had undergone at St. Vincent's in Santa Fe in October and at the family clinic in August. Apparently, this was standard operating procedure.

"I think it's an anxiety attack caused by the drug," I suggested to Dr. Burnett while Linda was gone.

"You could be right," he agreed. My medical quotient was improving. "I should have been a doc," I thought to myself.

The chest X-ray and EKG were normal, just as in Santa Fe. And, as it had been in Sante Fe, her white cell count was elevated, indicating some infection.

Dr. Burnett explained to Linda that he felt she might be having a reaction to the Lorabid. "She thinks she's dying," I told him. He smiled at Linda. "You're not dying."

She was relieved to be told this by a doctor. His opinion, backed by years of training and experience, carried more weight than mine.

"Of course," said Dr. Burnett, I want you to stop taking the Lorabid immediately."

"Don't worry," said my wife, who was regaining life with rapidity.

"She has an appointment with Dr. Silvers tomorrow. He's the one who prescribed it. Should we keep the appointment?" I asked.

Dr. Burnett was obviously uncomfortable with the question. He hesitated. I could sense he wanted to say "no." But, as a good member of the club he said, "You should probably follow up with him."

If medicine worked like my former profession, the insurance business, if there were some competition involved, the gentle Burnett might have handled it like this: *"Silvers is a pretty good knife man and when the eye goes down and you're left with a big flap of loose skin, he might be the guy you'll want to see to trim it up. But you've got a little mystery here that may be just out of his area of expertise. I've had excellent success with these strange ailments, and I've dealt with a few spider bites. If you want to, you can keep running all over town looking for answers. Right now, though, you need someone to act as your quarterback, as we may need to get some other physicians involved. You'll find that my office staff is very helpful and courteous and have the patient's interest at heart. Why don't you come by my office tomorrow at noon? I'll skip lunch and fit you in. In fact, I'll take you both to lunch. My first consultation is free."*

"You should probably follow up with Dr. Silvers," said Burnett without sincerity.

We walked slowly out of the hospital. "Do you feel better?" I asked her. "Yes," she replied. "I'm glad we went."

"I liked Dr. Burnett," I said. "He seemed to be a reasonable guy."

"He had a nice attitude," said Linda. "He didn't make me feel like I was nuts for thinking I was dying."

"Anxiety attacks can seem very real," I said conversationally.

"It was real. I wasn't faking."

"I know that."

"It was real," she said again.

"Really real," I said. "Real enough to cost $500."

"Is that all you care about?" she asked. "The money."

"Of course not. Insurance will cover most of it. It's just that I don't see that we learned too much for $500."

Linda went to bed. I called my brother. Dr. Bart Smith is a chiropractor who lives and practices in Honolulu. We often relied on him for information on health.

"We've been to the emergency room again," I told him.

"Has she been taking the stuff I sent her?" Bart wanted to know.

Bart was always telling us to take different stuff—like horsetail root and Dr. Jensen's "Whole Food Supplement." Most of the time we did.

"I think she might have candida," he said.

"What's candida?" I asked.

"It's a yeast overgrowth in your system. Didn't you get that book I told you about?"

"What book?"

I didn't know if I wanted to read another of his books. The last book he made us read was *Tissue Cleansing Through Bowel Management* by Dr. Bernard Jensen, a chiropractor and nutritionist. My brother had become an avid disciple of Dr. Jensen's regimen of raw foods and a clean bowel. Dr. Jensen has studied health practices around the world and written numerous books on nutrition. He worked with the famous Dr. John Harvey Kellogg of the Battle Creek Sanitarium. *Tissue Cleansing Through Bowel Management* is a book many people would rather not look at or think about. In the back are many color pictures showing close-ups of ropy globs of dark green fecal material reported to have arrived in the photos via someone's rectum. The normal reaction to the photos is to scream, slam the book shut, and deny the possibility.

My brother, Bart, had undergone the Jensen tissue cleansing regimen more than once. "You wouldn't believe the stuff that comes out," he said. "You should do it." I didn't believe it. I didn't want to do it.

Dr. Jensen believes a clean bowel is the first key to good health. Without a clean bowel, nutrients cannot be absorbed properly and the clog causes waste material to back up into the system resulting in autointoxication (self-poisoning). The Jensen program involved cleansing the bowel, during a seven-day period of fasting, using a technique called the colema, which is a combination of the words—colonic and enema.

A colema board is a specially-designed fiberglass board long enough to lie down on. On one end is a hole surrounded by a semi-circular splash shield. The hole goes over the toilet. Hanging above the board is a five-gallon bucket which has a plastic tube connected to it. At the end of the tube is a plastic tip, smaller than a little finger, which is lubricated and inserted into the rectum. A small clamp controls the gravity flow of water. Opening the clamp allows water to flow into the bowel. Amazingly, the fecal matter will bypass the tip. The tip doesn't have to be removed until the entire five gallons have been exhausted, which takes about thirty minutes. Note: the entire five gallons doesn't go into the rectum at one time. It's flowing in and out—like the tide.

A few months before we moved to Oregon, Linda had decided that a colema program might do her some good. She suffered no undue discomfort from fasting and she did not find the colema uncomfortable. However, the amount of material expelled, even through the end of the seven-day fasting period, was disconcerting. It was, in fact, unbelievable. Bart had closely monitored Linda's program via telephone. "What's it look like?" he had asked her on his first call. "I haven't looked," she answered. "Get your chopsticks out and look at it," he ordered.

The material did not look anything like feces. It was hard and rubbery. It was amazing, incredible. Linda felt good. She felt cleansed.

I had resisted but then decided to go for it. I stripped and locked the bathroom door. In Dr. Jensen's book the person modeling for the photos has ugly legs and ugly sandals. As I climbed onto my board holding my KY-jellied colema tip, I realized that Miss America would look ugly on a colema board. At 6'2", I didn't fit as comfortably on the board as Linda had. It was awkward but necessary to push my butt up to the splash shield after inserting the plastic tip. *"Use Great Caution. Insert plastic rectal tip no more than 3 inches past the anus because the distance between the anus and the bend in the bowel where the sigmoid flexure joins the rectum is only about five inches in most persons and less in some.* The plastic tip was aimed through a hole in the splash shield. It took a bit of coordination to hook up—kind of like a fighter plane hooking up to a tanker.

At first the colema itself was kind of fun. It wasn't painful. If, after intaking a quantity of water, I felt some discomfort, I put the clamps on it and the water flowed out. Surprisingly, it was difficult to even feel the "material" as it was expelled. There was a kind of fluttering feeling, like minnows swimming downstream, and a plop, plop, plop. Painless.

The nightmarish thing about the colema was the amount of material which continued to be expelled after seven days of fasting. Even on the fourteenth colema, on the seventh day, the seventieth gallon of water retrieved greenish ropy twists of expellant. It was a bad dream. A never-ending chain of fecal matter, mucous strands, toxic globs, and assorted crap was emerging at the very end. I quit, not knowing for certain that I was cleansed.

"Have you ever seen anything like it?" asked Bart.

"Never!" I answered.

"Never!" agreed Linda.

We felt good about the colemas but were left with the nagging feeling that there might be more where that came from. It was a monster movie unlike any other.

"Your grandmother was a great believer in colonics," reported my Mom. We were carrying on a family tradition.

With the colema experience in mind, our first unwitting adventure into the world of natural medicine, I was reluctant to embark on another of Dr. Bart's scenarios. We decided to see the ears, nose, and throat specialist again as half-heartedly recommended by Dr. Burnett.

We revisited Dr. Silvers. He was baffled. The sinus X-rays were clear. "It will probably go away," he said, charging us $40 for the visit.

"Do these guys ever say, 'There'll be no charge for this visit because I didn't do anything for you or tell you anything you needed or wanted to know?'" I asked, rhetorically, as we drove back through town. "No way!"

Linda was becoming very discouraged. In the past, antibiotics had always worked. One took the entire prescription and got on with one's life. And the eye! The eye was looking bad. The eyelid and the skin above it was bulging. Now it was beginning to swell beneath the eye. She looked like a boxer who had been severely beaten.

By this time she had seen Dr. Elias twice, Dr. Lewis once, Dr. Silvers twice, and Dr. Burnett in the emergency room, plus a dentist, an oral surgeon, and an endodontist. We decided to regroup and visit Burnett, a family practitioner. Of the four medical doctors we'd had on the case, we liked him best. How we felt about the doctor was the only rating system we or anyone else had available. There was no other method available to laymen to evaluate the performance, competence, or effectiveness of physicians.

Up until now I had been the chauffeur, sitting in waiting rooms with *People Magazine,* hopeful that Linda would get the problem solved. I decided I needed to get involved and went into the exam room with her at Dr. Burnett's office. Dr. Burnett was casual in chinos and sport shirt. Instead of a tie he wore a stethoscope. I repeated the case history relieving Linda of this verbal burden.

Burnett listened carefully to the story of the bite and the recap on the teeth. He showed no reaction to my report on Elias, Silvers and Lewis.

"Dr. Lewis didn't even look at it," interrupted Linda. Dr. Burnett took this cue and gave the eye a very careful look using a light and some kind of magnifying device. He asked questions like, "Have you traveled to any foreign countries?" Dr. Burnett decided it was an allergic reaction. "We'll make you an appointment with Dr. Conway in Medford. He's an excellent allergist. If it is an allergy, Dr. Conway will figure it out. He's very good."

Dr. Burnett's office made the appointment for us. It was December 17. Conway was so busy we couldn't see him until January 4. Linda was upset. She would have to wait for three weeks. In the meantime, Dr. Burnett ordered a blood test to see if there was anything unusual. He called personally a few days later to see how Linda was and to tell her the blood test was pretty normal. He was a nice fellow. But he had resorted to the "hand off."

Linda was toughing it out. She had headaches, a sharp pain in her eye, and her left cheekbone was sore and tender. She was staying in bed for longer periods of time. She ached and her chest hurt. She was out of commission. I reconsidered and began to read Bart's latest recommended book, *The Yeast Syndrome*, by John Trowbridge, M.D.

Before I read Trowbridge, I believed that all medical doctors practiced in essentially the same way. There were family physicians who treated general health, and in serious cases they would direct their patients to the proper specialists. Medicine had apparently become so complicated that specialists were required for each part of the body. Thus, we had heart, eye, lung, brain, urinary, reproductive, and bone specialists and even subspecialists like orthopods who did hands, or heart guys who did by-passes and balloon jobs. Then there were the technicians—radiologists and anesthesiologists and nuclear medicine specialists. All of these, I presumed, belonged to the American Medical Association. They were the mainstream of medicine who clustered around and practiced in the big hospitals, which appeared in every city that could figure out a way to build one. Allied with the doctors and nurses were the dentists and oral surgeons. Dentists seemed to be held in high regard because they had effectively eliminated tooth decay in our time.

At the edge of the medical circle were osteopaths and podiatrists. I assumed that an osteopath was a medical doc who could also adjust the spine and that podiatrists were limited to treating from the ankle down.

On the fringe were chiropractors who dealt with spinal manipulation and would, in extreme cases, claim to be able to deal with many health problems by adjusting subluxations of the spine. Chiropractors were not accepted into mainstream medical society while osteopaths and podiatrists seemed to be tolerated. Dr. Trowbridge surprised me because he found fault with the medical establishment and quoted other medical doctors who were likewise critical. Trowbridge criticized "medicrats" (medical bureaucrats), the *New England Journal of Medicine*, the misuse of antibiotics in humans and in animals, and the scientifically sacred double-blind controlled clinical studies.

His book was about Candida albicans, a fungus present in all human bodies. According to Dr. Trowbridge, the large intestine is five feet long and is a wet, moist, dark breeding ground for fungus, bacteria, and virus. It is a world where as many as five hundred varieties of organisms live. There are eighty-one different strains of yeast with C. albicans dominating the other strains. In this ecosystem there is a balance between good and bad microorganisms. Many events can upset this balance, prolonged use of antibiotics being one of them. Dr. Trowbridge writes:

". . .antibiotics also kill the friendly Lactobacilli which live synergystically in your intestines and keep down the spread of the Candida organism. . .Different antibiotics act against different microbes. Those that are effective against a great number of microbes are called broad spectrum antibiotics; these are the ones most likely to stimulate the illness–producing overgrowth of C. albicans. . .Antibiotic use disrupts the normal competition between the separate members of the resident flora of a human being's gut. . .The wholesale use of antibiotics for every little infection such as mild illnesses in children has negative consequences not immediately obvious. . .broad spectrum antibiotics are routinely added to animal feeds to promote more rapid and enhanced meat production in nearly all domestic edible animals. . .General agreement exists that antibiotic use is responsible for the record rise in resistant bacteria."

At least we didn't eat meat. But, to this point in a twelve month period, Linda had taken five full courses of antibiotics, three of

Amoxicillin, one of Tetracycline, and one of Erythromycin plus a partial course of the heinous Lorabid, the drug which sent her to the emergency room.

Dr. Trowbridge also believed that pollutants and poisons promote the "yeast syndrome" by creating stress which suppresses the immune system response. He listed several pages of items which could adversely affect one's internal ecology such as deodorants, asbestos, dust, natural gas furnaces, moldy food, detergents, water pipes, noise, household cleaners, radiation, house plants, drinking water, cat hair, and cat dander. We had all of the above. Linda was worried about the water. We had a reverse-osmosis water purifier installed under the kitchen sink. She was concerned about molds and dust and asbestos. In the middle of a December night, I undertook an asbestos abatement program and removed from our heating vent outlets what appeared to be some type of asbestos insulation. I stuffed it in a paper sack and carefully vacuumed the openings.

She was cold and worried that we couldn't keep the house warm enough. There was no sunlight in the winter on our shady side of the hill. She felt the damp. This had been a concern when we first bought the house and we had spent a considerable amount on weatherization, installing new thermopane windows and insulating the attic space. To insulate under the floor, the crawl space had to be excavated. The workman had to lay on his stomach and use a jack hammer to loosen the dirt. Dust had filled the house. Before we moved in, it had been thoroughly cleaned but Linda was convinced that dust seeped up through the wall to wall carpeting.

We replaced our forced air furnace. It filled the rooms with warm air but it was too hot or too cold. Our fireplace was plumbed for gas, and we went to Smokey's Fireplace shop and bought a free-standing gas stove. It was a Swedish Jotul, a lovely blue ceramic sculpture which radiated a consistent heat into the living room. Smokey installed it the week before Christmas. Linda and her cats were in love with the Jotul. She moved into the living room and slept on a futon, wrapped in quilts and lulled by purring.

"Maybe we should have the carpet removed," said Linda.

"Let's wait awhile," I suggested.

Dr. Trowbridge was explaining to me that candida normally lives by eating dead tissue rather than living matter. Taking antibiotics tends to turn the candida into a pathogen which eats living tissue.

Diet is a big issue in dealing with candida. To be avoided are yeast-containing foods such as bread, sugar (sucrose or fructose), dried fruits (which are often moldy), milk products other than yogurt, and white flour products such as pasta. Linda, I noted, was even more passionate about sweets than usual.

Dr. Trowbridge claimed that 30 percent of all persons around the world above the age of twelve were suffering with overgrowth of Candida albicans. Most of these people were women. Candida invasion could cause a plethora of symptoms including headaches, indigestion, nausea, abdominal pain, diarrhea, constipation, dizziness, fatigue, lethargy, white-coated tongue, giant hives, skin eruptions, inadequate nutrient assimilation, nearly every type of allergic reaction, anxiety, depression, asthma, and other respiratory tract disorders. We were familiar by now with much of the above.

Bart had sent a bottle of Caprystatin and another of Capricin. Trowbridge explained in the book that these were nutritional supplements of caprylic acid which had been found to restore and maintain a normal balance of yeast, bacteria, and other organisms in the colon. Linda began to take these two supplements. Bart had warned of a "die-off" reaction. The die-off occurs when the C. albicans cells are killed and release toxins into the system causing violent symptoms to occur. This is also known as the "Herxheimer reaction," as it was originally described by a German dermatologist. The Herxheimer reaction can last for a few days or—bad news—even weeks resulting in so much discomfort for some patients that they have to reduce or discontinue treatment. The "die-off" is considered evidence that the treatment is working.

Herxheimer quickly appeared in our living room and wrapped Linda in a covering of flu-like symptoms. She was miserable. She ached all over, was hot and cold, and had a headache. I read the section to her about die-off reaction. Bart talked to her on the phone, encouraging her to hang in.

It was Christmastime. We didn't decorate. She wanted to participate in the Christmas festivities but didn't have the energy. We did no Christmas shopping, proof of her unwellness. Our good friends, Dan and Marie, came to stay for the holidays. They were easy to have as company. Dan, a Registered Nurse, was alarmed by the eye. He thought it was cellulitis.

Linda mustered enough strength to walk down the hill to town. Ashland was decorated in tiny white lights which outlined the buildings in the business district. Dan bought fudge. I warned Linda about eating it. Sugar feeds the yeast. She ate some anyway. The next night, Christmas Eve, I invited friends to come over. Linda survived the party and slept late.

Mt. Ashland was offering free skiing to celebrate the reopening of the mountain under community ownership. Dan wanted to ski. Marie and I drove Dan up to the mountain and dropped him off. When we returned Linda was gone. On the kitchen counter was a note:

"*I've gone to the Emergency Room. Don't worry, I'm okay. Love, Linda.*"

Marie and I were at the hospital in five minutes flat. Linda was sitting on the examining room table.

"Are you all right?" I asked her.

"I thought I was going to faint," she said. "I felt really bad."

A Dr. Marks was presiding today.

"Her white cell count is up," he said. "So I'm going to prescribe an antibiotic."

"She's had a lot of antibiotics," I told him.

"Eat tons of yogurt," he told her, "and take some echinacea. It's an herb that boosts the immune system. I'm also going to set you up for a CAT scan to make sure nothing strange is going on behind the eye. I don't think there's a tumor," he said, "but let's make sure."

In the waiting room Marie gave Linda a big hug. "You scared us," she told her.

"I started worrying about things," Linda whispered.

"Like tumors," I thought to myself.

The next day Dan and Marie went home and I picked up the Keflex Marks had prescribed. On the 29th we went back to Radiology for a CAT scan. For the next two days we tried to get the results. No one would give us the information. We called Marks but couldn't reach him. We called Burnett and his office checked with the radiologist who, for some reason, would not talk to us directly. Finally, we got a call from Dr. Elias, the ophthalmologist. He reported that the CAT scan results had been sent to his office.

"They're clear," he said. "No problems. No tumors."

Linda noticeably relaxed when Dr. Elias reported, "No tumors."

It had been six weeks since Linda had seen Elias.

"I feel really bad that you're still dealing with this thing," he told me. "I'm leaving for Tibet for three weeks but I'd like your wife to see my new partner. I can get you in this afternoon."

It was nice of Elias to be concerned so we hopped in the car and drove to see Dr. Green, who was fresh off the faculty of a famous medical school. He examined her eye.

"The eyeball is fine," he told us. "It must be some kind of allergic reaction."

"We're seeing an allergist next week."

"That's a good idea," said Dr. Green. His charge for the ten minute session was $28.

It was the 31st of December. In this very medical year, Linda had experienced a dental operation on an abscessed root canal, had a root-canaled tooth extracted, taken seven courses of antibiotics, been to emergency rooms three times, had two EKGs, two chest X-rays, sinus X-rays, full-jaw X-rays, a CAT scan, three blood tests, and seen eight different medical doctors. Her eye was still greatly swollen. She felt sicker than ever. We had no diagnosis.

LINDA'S VOICE: *I was frantic to know what was wrong. Bart had me call Chayla, his psychic friend. She asked about our trip to Arizona. Suggested it might be Valley Fever, picked up from dust and pollen. . .weakens immune system. . .affects all parts of the body. . .cold damp weather weakens the immune system. . .keep warm and dry–exercise–oxygenate. . .cold, wet not good–TOXIC. Chest attacked. . .dried out inside chest and head. . .mucous lining where air comes in attacked–no heating pads or other electric implements. . .cold weather not healthy. . .body cringing. . .not healthy for me. . .summers okay. . .no cold air. . .bones achey, overload of toxins. . .immune system going down. . .don't eat or drink cold. . .lots of water. . .collect information from everyone. . .take B-12 and Vitamin D.*

The new year would prove that we were just getting started on our adventure. The year ended with Linda in the living room. Her furry cat, Sam, was sitting behind her on the back of the couch. Sam was quietly studying Linda's head when suddenly he leaned forward and bit her twice on the scalp. Linda turned to her kitty with a look of shock. Then she began to cry.

Chapter 4
Searching for Wellville

It was a new year. Our long-anticipated appointment with the allergist arrived and we drove to Medford—fifteen miles up the freeway. Everything about the Conway Allergy & Asthma Clinic, P.C. was impressive, beginning with the excellent selection of magazines in the large, well-appointed waiting area. While we waited, a parade of people came and went—a brief rendezvous with a nurse, a shot for their allergy, and on their way. Burnett and Marks were so high on Conway's abilities that I confidently decided to remain in the waiting room of this wellness center to read *Smithsonian Magazine.* The chairs were more comfortable than normal. The nurse called for Linda. Linda gave me a quick smile and walked slowly forward, sunglasses in place, in search of a healer.

It was clear that Conway had quite an operation going, and I began to count the visitors who arrived for shots or examinations. There were lots of children, and I noted that the clinic was for adult and pediatric allergies. He had an excellent patient information brochure, which communicated the gist of his practice in friendly terminology:

Welcome to our clinic.
It is our pleasure to serve you.
I am qualified. . .
Two visits to complete exam. . .
I am a specialist in Allergy-Immunology. . .
Degree from Iowa. . .
Appointments two months in advance. . .
I will return your calls. . .
Emergencies dealt with immediately. . .
On the staff at both hospitals.
Our fees are fair and reasonable.

Pay at the time of visit. . .
We don't bill insurance.

The brochure even had an "Epilogue," the first I'd ever seen in a brochure. In the epilogue Dr. Conway pointed out that we needed to understand the nature of our treatments and options, the names of our medications, and how to use them. He closed as follows: *"My purpose, and that of our entire office staff, is to aid you in every way possible to attain this knowledge and maintain your optimum state of health."*

I'd written a couple of brochures myself and this one was well done. It was clear and concise and communicated the essence of the Conway Clinic. Clearly, this doctor had respect for the intelligence of his patients. My hope index increased.

An hour passed and I familiarized myself with many of his patients. They all looked like they were feeling pretty well. This waiting room was healthier than many. A nurse called my name, and I was led through clinical corridors to an exam room where a smiling Linda sat on a table dressed in an exam gown.

"Look at my back," she said.

It looked as if someone had poked her with pins and then written on her with a pen.

"I'm allergic to dust mites," she said happily. "The doctor started to explain it to me but I asked him to tell you too."

"Dust mites," I said. "We saw pictures of them in *National Geographic*, remember? The pictures were taken with an electron microscope, and they looked like dinosaur monsters."

Dr. Conway, the allergist, breezed into the room and shook my hand. He was friendly and efficient and appeared to be just as bright as his colleagues said he was. He looked as if he had been the smartest kid in his high school, winner of the Science Fair prize, and manager of the basketball team, dateless for the prom, but no doubt now lived in a big house in the country with a good-looking wife who liked horses.

"So, it's dust mites, huh?" I said.

Dr. Conway stood squarely in front of us. I was now seated next to Linda on the exam table. I was prepared to receive a short course in dust mites.

"Actually, what you see here," said Dr. Conway pointing to Linda's swollen eye is urticaria—commonly known as hives."

"Aahh," we both said like a Greek chorus. "Hives!"

"Hives," continued the doctor "are itchy welt-like lesions on the skin. They're very common. At some point in their lives about 20 percent of the population will have them. Most hives are called acute hives," he said, emphasizing "acute." "Acute hives are easily triggered by viral infections, foods, medications, or emotional changes and they last six to eight weeks. Sometimes acute hives have no easily identifiable cause. Because acute hives are self-limited and because extensive tests often don't tell us what they are, I usually direct my attention to treatment rather than investigation."

"Do you think the eye is caused by dust mites?" I asked.

Doctor Conway was gathering steam and only nodded toward my question. "Hives are caused by the inappropriate release of vasoactive mediators. These are chemicals that cause blood vessels in the skin to dilate and become very porous, leaking large quantities of fluid into the skin. This causes the redness and swelling. Many vasoactive mediators affect the nerve endings, as well. This causes itching. Several vasoactive mediators may be involved in hives including histamine, kinins, prosteglandins, leukotrienes, and others. They are usually produced in small quantities by processes that regulate other events in the body."

Linda and I were smiling. Conway knew his stuff all right.

"Examples of these processes are mast cells, kinin system, arachadonic acid metabolism, and others."

He stopped talking and with his ballpoint pen drew us a clever picture of a mast cell which seemed to be full of little circles representing vasoactive chemicals. Some other little circles were moving toward the mast cell, which then produced a histamine. The histamine, which appeared to look like a small piece of Lego, floated off the mast cell and coupled with another piece of Lego which was attached to a blood vessel. I held the drawing in my hand trying to comprehend the microcosm of Linda's cells as Dr. Conway continued his disquisition.

"Normally, the amounts of vasoactive mediators released are too small to be noticed, but in hives something has gone wrong resulting in release of larger than normal amounts of histamine and other vasoactive mediators. There are lots of possible causes of the release of these vasoactive chemicals that cause hives. For example, they could be caused by inflammatory diseases like lupus."

Linda gave a quick look of alarm. We knew something about lupus. We had a good friend who had lupus. We didn't want lupus.

"Or, it could be an infection. Sometimes they're caused by thyroid disease, or tumors. They could be inherited. Hives can be triggered by physical factors such as cold. Allergies to inhaled materials, foods, or drugs are surprisingly not common causes of chronic hives. But, in this case, I believe it is the dust mites."

"Will the hives go away?" asked Linda.

Dr. Conway continued his discourse on hives in spite of this interruption.

"I'm prescribing several medications," he said. "The first is Atarax which is an antihistamine. I will also give you some eye drops to relieve itching. Finally, I'll give you a short course of Prednisone. You'll take two pills a day for three days. Then one pill per day for three days. This is a cortisone drug and can have some dramatic side effects. But very short courses don't create these problems. Prednisone may, however, cause stomach irritation, fluid retention, increased appetite, or mood swings. But," he said with a smile, "I think you'll see a dramatic effect on your eye!"

Linda smiled brightly. This was what she had been waiting to hear. "I'm going to have you get some additional blood work and I'll also order all the blood work, you've already had sent over to my office. We'll need to have you sign some forms. Now, I'm going to ask the nurse to come in and talk to you about how to manage house dust mites. She will give you a very complete overview. Use your best judgment on the measures you take to reduce exposure to these critters. You don't need to go overboard."

"Any questions?" he asked. We had none.

"I'll see you in two weeks," said Conway over his shoulder as he strode out the door.

As Dr. Conway walked out we felt like giving him a standing ovation. He had actually taken the time to explain to us what was taking place in Linda's body. He sure knew his stuff. We were thankful to Dr. Burnett for sending us there.

The nurse came in and with no small talk began her briefing on dust mites.

"Your allergy evaluation has shown you are allergic to house dust. I think Doctor probably explained how it connects to an allergy antibody and sets off an allergic chemical reaction."

We nodded in the affirmative.

"Mast cells," said Linda.

"Vasoactive mediators," I said brightly.

She handed us a brochure showing an electron microscopic photo of a dust mite. We recoiled in horror. The six-legged monster with a pincher on its head and big hairy things sticking from his legs, walked across the page and into our consciousness.

"These are microscopic insect-like creatures found in the home. They live primarily in mattresses, carpets, and upholstered furniture. The mite's diet consists of shed scales of human skin."

"Ick!" said Linda.

"What you are actually allergic to is waste product particles produced by these mites."

"Waste product particles," I said. "Would that be shit?" My little attempt at a joke fell flat. This nurse was seriously into dust mites.

"Each mite produces about twenty particles of feces per day. Now female mites lay twenty-five to fifty eggs, and a new batch is produced every three weeks. So there can be literally millions of dust mites living in your home."

"Millions times twenty particles," I thought to myself.

The nurse handed us a checklist. "Though it is impossible to completely avoid house dust, it is possible to minimize exposure. This is important in order to maximize benefit from your medications. Emphasis should be placed on the bedroom."

She led us through the checklist. It was overwhelming:

1) All dust sources and dust catchers should be eliminated.
This includes essentially any objects that collect dust (books, toys, knick-knacks, etc). Objects in the room should have a smooth hard surface and should be dusted regularly.

—A small number of books in enclosed book shelves are permissible.

—The bedroom closet should be used only to store clothes used regularly in the present season. Others should be encased in plastic and stored in other parts of the house.

2) **Bed**

a) Mattress, box springs, and all pillows should be completely encased by **impermeable plastic covers** that zip closed. These may be obtained through most major department stores.

(Less "plastically feeling" but more expensive coverings are available from Allergy Control Products. . .1-800-422-DUST. They will also send you advertising for many products that may not be needed for your house dust allergy. Discuss with us before ordering these).

b) Waterbeds are okay but the frames must be dusted regularly. Do not use bunk beds.

c) You may use a fitted polyester mattress pad over the plastic covers. Wash it with the bedding.

d) **Pillows** should be Dacron or polyester.

e) All **bedding** should be of washable synthetic material and **should be washed weekly** (including mattress pad, sheets, blankets, bedspreads, and pillow cases).

—Do not use nonwashable bedspreads.

—If electric blankets are needed, they may be placed between two sheets while on the bed to minimize dust collection. Hand rinse blankets in water monthly to remove dust.

3) **Curtains** should be washable and washed weekly. Window shades are preferable to venetian blinds.

4) **Vinyl or wood floors** are the most easily cleaned, short pile carpet a little more difficult, and shag much more difficult. Do not replace floor material without discussing it with us. It is not necessary for many people.

5) **Clean** the bedroom thoroughly **once a week** and lightly **wet dust daily**.

6) **Keep windows closed.** Do not use fans.

7) **Forced air heat vents** should be kept closed as much as is compatible with comfort. They may also be covered with three to five layers of cheesecloth. **Change furnace filters monthly.**

8) **Do not humidify your home**, especially if you are allergic to house dust mites.

I visualized a life of drudgery in our battle against the mighty mite who was trying to kill us with his feces. I wondered if I would ever be able to sleep well again or if the deafening noise of millions of dust mites chewing my dead skin cells would keep me awake eternally.

The nurse gave us a brochure which listed products used to control allergy: mattress covers, comforter covers, box spring protectors, pillows and cases, blankets, air cleaners and filters, dust masks, vacuum cleaners, electrostatic filters, and several books.

"This is for your information," said the nurse. "The Conway Clinic receives no compensation from this company."

We paid our bill. It was $196. We picked up $160 worth of medications at the pharmacy. When we got home, we decided to order a mattress cover ($64.95), a pillow case ($12.95), a comforter cover ($76), and a box spring protector ($35). We would make our bed into a defensive position and try to hold off the horde of mites who lay in siege.

LINDA'S VOICE: *Today I drank hot chocolate all day. Read Noble's textbooks on makeup and costume history. Shawn came over. He is so sweet. When he can, he comes on his lunch hour and holds my arm while we walk around the back yard. He thinks exercise is the thing. I can hardly stand up. Feel so weak. Don't really want the boys to know how sick I am. We all had Randy's homemade soup—yummy. I sat by the fire and thought. I finally feel like I'm healing from this long illness. The pains in my chest. The aching muscles. The sad eye. Sad eye. The swelling seems to be going away—very gradually. The redness is almost gone. This is my fifth day on prednisone. No noticeable side effects except improved appetite. Sleeping a lot. No mind trips like that terrible antibiotic. Randy made a great Mexican lasagna. Am I still alive? I want to be well. Recovery, Recovery, Recovery. It's 10p.m.—time for bed. . .R. is taking a quick shower. How do I feel? Better, Lighter, Hopeful, Fatter. I did my nails. Things are looking up. Good night; Sweet Dreams Little Lost Child.*

Linda took the Prednisone as prescribed. The eye swelling went down slightly, but not significantly. We returned to Conway's Clinic the following week. Linda still felt very ill. Dr. Conway was shocked that there had been no clear improvement. He now expressed doubt that this was an allergic reaction. Dr. Conway had reviewed all the blood tests and they were normal. He threw in the towel and went for a handoff. He had his secretary call a Dr. Youngman, a dermatologist located up the street. If we hurried he could see Linda immediately. If Dr. Youngman didn't know the answer, we might have to do a biopsy.

We paid $35 to get out of the Conway Clinic and drove up the street to Youngman's. I stayed in the waiting room. Dr. Youngman, Linda reported, did not know what the problem was but thought she had really nice skin. He took two photos of her eye. He thought it might be something like poison oak and asked her what kind of house plants she had. He told her to keep her hands out of her eyes. He felt that Conway's 20 mg. Prednisone prescription had not been strong enough and wrote her another for "Prednisone 50 mg. #7." We paid him $80.

Sitting in the car, Linda started to sob and ripped the prescription into little pieces. We were back where we'd started.

Driving through Ashland with a sobbing woman was getting to be a routine. "People are going to think I'm beating you," I told Linda. "Someone's going to call the cops. I won't be able to show my face."

My weak attempt at humor didn't help. She continued to cry. "Look," I said, "We're not giving up on this. Someone has to have the answer. We'll figure out what to do." Linda went to bed. I sat in the living room and tried to conjure a solution. One additional problem was looming. Our insurance would expire in six months. Having retired, I was on COBRA (referring to the federal law which required our previous group insurer to continue coverage on us for a total of eighteen months from my retirement date). We'd used twelve of those months. Because any new insurance policy that we might buy would have a preexisting condition exclusion, any disease Linda had as of the date of the new insurance would not be covered under the new program. To have insurance coverage we needed to identify the problem and solve it before July 1, 1993. It was now January 19. (While I was pondering, a large package arrived from Allergy Control Products, Inc. We sent it back unopened.)

Linda, in addition to feeling poorly, was very depressed. She sensed that something was wrong with her cheek because of tenderness there and she worried about her liver. I was not sure of the source of her liver concern other than intuition. The CAT scan had alleviated fears about a tumor behind her eye, but I still worried that we could be financially ruined by a yet unnamed disease. It seemed inconceivable that a person could feel so unwell and that eight or nine highly-qualified physicians could do so little to identify the source of the ailment. The cost of evaluating and treatment to this point had been significant. Fortunately, most of it had been reimbursed by insurance. To this point we had dealt with the mainstream medical establishment. It was what we were familiar with, and the procedures of medical doctors and the medications they prescribed were covered by insurance. We had considered seeing a naturopathic doctor recommended by our dentist and had even scheduled an appointment. I had filled out an exhaustive questionnaire and had delivered it to the naturopathic doctor's office. This doctor was extremely busy and semi-retired. I had asked his secretary if they would call us in the event of a cancellation. They never got the questionnaire. I later found out that their postman had removed the unstamped envelope which I had left in their mailbox. He had taken it to his supervisor who, following U.S. Postal Service instructions, destroyed it. By the time I figured this out, a week had passed and we were still waiting for a cancellation. The first visit to this naturopath was several hundred dollars, not covered by insurance, but we were willing to pay it.

We had a close friend who had been suffering from lupus for several years. We had watched her decline with alarm and concern. Recently she had been feeling better and she attributed her improvement to a local physician, a medical doctor named Will Jordan who she reported practiced "holistically." We didn't know what that meant. But Linda decided she wanted to see Dr. Jordan as soon as possible. We scheduled a visit with Dr. Jordan and canceled our appointment with the naturopath which was still a month away. Jordan could see us immediately. And, his services were covered by our insurance plan.

Dr. Jordan was warm and friendly. He was, it seemed, accessible. He ushered us into an office full of books. He sat at his desk and we were seated in side chairs. A small exam table was pushed against the wall next to the door. The atmosphere was casual. It didn't seem necessary to call him "Doctor." Will was wearing a long-sleeved striped dress shirt, button-down collar, and knit tie. He sat back in his chair and held a pencil in both hands. He was my age, I guessed, or a bit younger but his hair was prematurely gray and he wore a mustache which framed a constant smile. While we were waiting for him in the outer office, I'd read a news clipping which indicated he had trained at UCLA and practiced in California. On his bookshelf were two books on Candida albicans (Trowbridge and Crook), books on nutrition, books on vitamins, and books on self-help.

He began to ask questions. He noted each answer which led to a next logical query. While we talked he carefully filled three pages with information. He focused in on the root canals. Linda believed her teeth were involved but no other doctor had seemed interested in her dental work. Dr. Jordan jumped to no conclusions, however. He questioned until it seemed he could think of nothing else to ask. He had found out everything Linda wanted to tell.

I expressed my concern about the number of courses of antibiotics Linda had taken. He felt that this was a problem, too, and that many of her symptoms were typical of Candida albicans. He told us that he used antibiotics if necessary, but hopefully as a last resort. He then explained how he hoped to get at the problem. This interview was step one. Then he would do blood work and urinalysis. Finally, he would ask Linda to provide a stool sample to test for fungus and parasites.

"She's had lots of blood work recently. Can't you use those tests?" I asked. Dr. Jordan explained that he did some lab work himself but also sent the work to labs outside of the area to conduct special tests. It was his guess that we would discover candida as a primary culprit.

"But what about my eye?" asked Linda.

"I've seen lots of eyes like that when I worked in an emergency room," said Dr. Jordan. "It's a classic allergic reaction. The unique thing about your case," he continued, "is that it only involves one eye. I think you should have your dentist look at that tooth again and see if it needs to be pulled. You should also find out what the material was in the root so we can determine if there's some type of allergic reaction to that substance."

During the interview we had explained that Linda's gum had abscessed and Dr. Vernon, the endodontist, had changed the material in the root.

"Well, the best thing may be to have it pulled."

"It will leave a big gap," I said.

"That can be fixed," said Jordan. "Now the other problems you're having are due to poor absorption of nutrients. When the candida takes over, your digestive system doesn't work as well, and food and medicines don't get absorbed into your bloodstream. We use intravenous techniques to counter that problem and can give you vitamins and supplements through a tube."

We had heard about the intravenous from our friend with lupus, who was making such great strides. When entering the doctor's private office, we had walked past a room full of big reclining chairs. Seated in the chairs were people taking intravenous feedings.

"You also show evidence of possible thyroid deficiencies, so I want to take your temperature every morning for a week. Take it under your arm as soon as you wake up."

"Dr. Jordan," I asked. "Are you a member of the American Medical Association?"

He smiled. "No," he said, "I'm not. I belong to a couple of organizations, though. One is the American Academy of Environmental Medicine."

"Are there many other doctors who practice like you do?"

"Quite a few," he replied. "More all the time, actually."

"How come we never hear about them? Why is it always the AMA?"

"It's really the pharmaceutical companies," he said. "They control the media. More importantly, they control the medical journals. If you look at a publication like the *New England Journal of Medicine* you'll see that most of the advertising support is from the drug companies. They aren't going to support a publication that criticizes drugs. So, our guys can't get anything published."

"I don't want to take any more drugs," said Linda.

"Hopefully, it won't be necessary. Now let's talk for awhile about how you feel about this situation," he said, focusing his attention on Linda.

"How I feel?" she said.

"How do you feel about being so sick and not getting any help?"

"I. . .I. . .I don't know," she said, struggling for an answer.

"Is it upsetting?" he asked.

"Yes, of course."

"Do you cry about it?"

"Yes, I cry. I cry a lot."

"You seem so pleasant about the whole situation. You're so nice. Aren't you angry with the run-around?" He was pressing here, which surprised me. But I didn't interrupt.

"I'm mad about it," she said.

"You don't seem very mad," said the doctor. "Is there some event, some traumatic event that has occurred recently which could be so upsetting as to make you become ill?"

"I don't think so," she said.

I did interrupt and explained about our change of life-style, the sale of our business interests, the move to Ashland from a whirligig of activity to a small town; from a big house to a small house;

from having a social and economic position in a community to becoming anonymous and, finally, the removal of her collections of hats and tins and art work to an inaccessible mini-storage.

"Do you think that could make her ill?" I asked him.

"It could. You see we are, essentially, just bundles of energy and there is an absolute linkage between the mind and the physical body. I really believe that one day we'll be able to cure the body by treating the mind, and the drugs and so forth that are so common today will be obsolete."

"Hmm," I said. I had no idea what he was talking about.

He asked Linda to get up on the exam table and checked her blood pressure, eyes and ears, and poked around her abdomen.

"Okay," he said, speaking directly to Linda, "here's how we're going to attack the problem. I'm going to have some blood drawn and we'll run several tests. We'll get a urine sample and test that. I'll give you a stool sample kit and you can send that off. While we're waiting for the test results we'll get you started on some intravenous vitamins and minerals to see if we can't boost your energy a bit. We'll also give you some antihistamines, a natural antihistamine, to see if we can get the eye to react. As soon as the tests are back, we'll get down to serious business and see if we can knock out whatever it is. Also, I want you to get another opinion on the tooth and see if you can find out what's in the root canal. Sound okay?"

"Sounds great," said Linda.

We'd been with Dr. Jordan for an hour and fifteen minutes. He'd collected the information he apparently needed. The charge was $100. Linda drove home holding her stool sample kit, sobbing with optimism. I took her back the next day for an intravenous treatment which we thought included Vitamin C, B vitamins, calcium, magnesium, and a natural antihistamine. The intravenous seemed to provide a short burst of energy and a sense of well-being. A week or so later Dr. Jordan called.

"This is Will Jordan," he said, "Is Linda there?"

"She's asleep," I told him. "This is her husband."

"I got her urinalysis done and she has an occult urinary tract infection. We need to get her on an antibiotic to knock it out."

He prescribed Noroxin and I walked down to the pharmacy to pick it up. I had been keeping track since the abscessed root canal and this was the eighth course of antibiotics, plus the Prednisone that Dr. Conway had given her. I had expressed my concern and Dr. Jordan suggested I come to his office and purchase some powerful acidophilus to help maintain the good flora in her system.

Linda was stalling on the stool sample, and I kept insisting that she get the sample and send it in. We were reduced to arguments about stools. The stool sample had a definite protocol. One was required to catch a little piece of waste before it was contaminated by the toilet water. Only the tiniest piece was required. A small wooden implement was included. The fecal tidbit was then transferred to a miniature Dixie cup which was placed in a larger container. That, in turn, went into a plastic pouch which was pre-addressed to the Great Smoky Laboratories somewhere back East. On the pouch were instructions to call Airborne Express who would appear to collect the pouch and carry it to the scientist who was to examine the sample particle. Caveats in the instructions were to check with Airborne for their schedule of pickups in the neighborhood prior to sampling because of the necessity for the stool to be fresh. Obviously, one could not take a sample on the weekend.

Finally, after much encouragement, the sample was reluctantly captured, and a lady from Airborne arrived and took it away from us. While we waited for the results, Linda continued frequent intravenous treatments. Dr. Jordan was thorough with his lab work. We had now bought a stool test, a urinalysis, an antibiotic sensitivity test, a CBC, an ESR, an automated chemical panel, and a liver screen. I felt good about Dr. Jordan and believed that he would identify the problem and find a solution. Instead of going into the office with Linda I would wait in the car or take a walk or drop her off and pick her up. It seemed that Linda had a doctor's appointment or a massage appointment every couple of days. In between, she rested or slept. She had lost interest in almost everything.

I had been trying to keep myself busy by researching an idea I had for a book which would be a walking guide to Ashland and its immediate environs. February is not unpleasant in Ashland but it is cold, and at higher elevations there is snow.

Linda was sleeping, resting, and being ill. I had to find something to do to fill the long blanks of time that she spent in bed. During that winter I made the acquaintance of Henry David Thoreau, who became my constant companion for the next few months. It was amazing to me that, as a liberal arts graduate of a well-regarded college, I had never, to my recollection, read more than an excerpt of *Walden*. My impression had been that Thoreau was tough reading. I was wrong. His writing was to provide me with a great amount of guidance and inspiration. In his essay on "Walking" Thoreau said, "We should go forth on the shortest walk. . .in the spirit of undying adventure, never to return—prepared to send back our embalmed hearts only as relics to our desolate kingdoms. . . .I think that I cannot preserve my health and spirits unless I spend four hours a day at least. . .sauntering through the woods and over the hills and fields, absolutely free from all worldly engagements."

Here was a man who believed walking was an heroic activity, who invoked a new chivalric spirit and likened his sauntering activity to knighthood. I was, of course, walking already but Henry taught me how to do it better. I followed him out to Walden Pond, up the Concord and Merrimack Rivers, through the Maine woods, and to Cape Cod. Henry was consumptive yet was more than willing to sleep in the rain or struggle through a damp swamp. His health was often poor, exacerbated by breathing wood dust from the family's pencil factory but it seemed not to dissuade him from his sauntering. "I can easily walk ten, fifteen, twenty, any number of miles," he bragged, "commencing at my own door. . .There are square miles in my vicinity which have no inhabitant. From many a hill I can see civilization and the abodes of man afar."

We had so much in common. I would not claim to twenty miles but I could walk ten, and as deer trails led from the oaky woods into our back yard, I could, like Henry, walk miles into the wilderness and from high points look down on civilization. And so while Linda slept through the winter and into spring, I stalked the woods with field guide and camera to botanize. Henry was an accomplished all-around naturalist. I was a beginner. In March I was drawn to a tall plant with dramatic leaves and a small but showy purple bloom—the hound's tongue, named for the shape of its leaves. I became a maniac for wildflowers and stalked them endlessly, returning to a spot to catch the perfect light, on guard always for poison oak which seemed to take on many different shapes and colors. I didn't keep a journal. I could not compete with Henry, but did learn from him to note small details and changes simply for the sake of noting them.

"If you are ready to leave father and mother, and brother and sister, and wife and child and friends, and never see them again," he said to me one day, "If you have paid your debts, and made your will, and settled all your affairs, and are a free man, then you are ready for a walk." I knew what he meant by this. It was not a literal statement. He meant that a good walker would be detached and at home anywhere. And if one walked with a spirit of adventure, one could break with the past and add new knowledge from the experience of walking.

Our medical journey was never far from my mind, and the curiosity I developed walking in the woods that season was soon transferred from flowers to the human system. In the woods, as spring broke through, there was an energy, a vitality which sometimes overpowered me. I left the trails and followed paths made by deer and was rewarded with sights no one else saw, spring-like fields of fawn lilies broadcasting color into the air. Each individual flower seemed to me a radiant force, and as the months of spring passed by, I found and photographed over a hundred different species. There was something mystical about our woods with its strange mixture of evergreen and deciduous trees: the oaks, the pine, the fir, the madrone, and manzanita bushes big as trees. I never saw anyone else once I left a trail. I was alone with the nature spirits, and they floated with me through the succession of plants.

I was not the only collector who had wandered these woods. Many years before, the novelist Vladimir Nabokov had rented a house just up the street from us and spent his days hunting butterflies in the hills above town and his nights working on the completion of *Lolita,* the book that would make him famous. His biographer noted that Nabokov could walk eighteen miles a day. Henry and Vladimir could make one feel inadequate as both walker and writer. Nabokov wrote a poem while in Ashland called, "Lines Penned in Oregon" which was published in the *New Yorker*. It is a mysterious magical poem which provides some dreamy Oregon images. It starts, "Esmiralda! Now we rest/ Here, in the bewitched and blest/ Mountain forests of the West." I was pleased that I was as bewitched as the well-known butterfly collector.

It was very strange to live with a person who was dormant. I had entertained a hope that in springtime Linda's sap would begin to run and that vitality would blossom. This was not to be. She would stay in bed for hours, then stay in bed some more. It was ironic. We had completely reorganized our lives to be able to recreate together. Instead, Linda was on her way to invalidism and I was virtually alone. I had never worried about what I would do when I no longer had to work and had laughed off comments that I wouldn't be able to stand the inactivity. There was plenty to do and to see. We had imagined daily walks and gardening, hikes in the mountains, and day trips. There were so many places of interest within a couple hours drive—Crater Lake, Mt. Shasta, the ocean, the redwoods, Oregon Caves. In Ashland itself was the Oregon Shakespeare Festival and several other theaters performing a total of over twenty plays a year. There were lectures and recitals at Southern Oregon State College. A movie theatre was within walking distance, as was the charming little village of Ashland where one could do a circuit on foot to bank, pay bills, post letters, and pick up a bag of groceries. We had envisioned life in an English village without having to leave America.

To be sure, I was enjoying some of it, but more and more of my time was occupied as caregiver and homemaker. I think I had always appreciated the role of homemaker but had certainly never understood the time demands of menu planning, shopping, cleaning, and cooking. Homemaking, I found, was a time-consuming activity. It was a difficult activity to organize efficiently. In my career as a manager I was familiar with the essential elements of running a business—planning, operating, controlling, etc. It seemed logical that these skills could be used effectively in running a home. I had a budget which I'd outlined on my computer and, for the first time I could remember, was keeping track of income and expenses to a level which resembled that of a business. Homemaking reminded me of the insurance business in many ways: 1) a job never seemed completed; and 2), there was no positive feedback. Unlike the insurance business, homemaking was not financially rewarding. The big difference was that I found homemaking strangely satisfying. I enjoyed cleaning up the kitchen, though it seemed perpetually messed up. I liked folding clean clothes and putting them in drawers. I even liked scrubbing out the bathroom. Vacuuming was a pleasure, window-washing a breeze. It was exhilarating to put a ladder up to the roof and clean the leaves out of the gutters and look out over the quiet town. . .the "civilization and abodes of man." In the distance was the horizontal stripe of Interstate 5 placed thankfully on the other side of the valley. Sitting on the roof one day I counted fifty-six big trucks pass a certain point in five minutes time. The world of commerce was passing me by. I didn't care. I returned to the house to wash the window blinds and dust the shelves.

What I didn't like about homemaking was the tyranny imposed by our collective stomachs. (Noble, our son, was back living with us while finishing college). I struggled to develop a system to maintain an adequate supply of nourishing food and snacks without going over the budget I had set. In spite of my planning, I was constantly on the run for groceries and although I had always done the food shopping for our family from a list prepared by Linda, the added responsibility of also preparing the food seemed to make the task more odious. I tried different techniques such as fast shopping—it wore me out—and team shopping with Noble—we tore the list in half and still forgot or duplicated items. I could not make the activity efficient. I tried shopping for a five-day menu, a two-day menu, and a seven-day menu. The two-day program sent me to the store too frequently. With the seven-day menu we always ran out of stuff and had to go back anyway. Finally, I settled on a four-day program as the method most compatible with my style. In addition, I decided to be a slow shopper, a label reader, a product studier. Ashland has a Community Food Store, purveyors of natural foods and organic produce, bulk grains and spices, olive oil and molasses from a spigot, fresh-squeezed juice, raw goat milk, rennet-less cheeses, oriental noodles, Middle Eastern flours, kohlrabi and burdock root, vitamins, supplements, homeopathic remedies, essential oils, and more. It became for me an institution of higher learning. I learned to make gobo with garlic, and that arnica was good for sore muscles. The food store became a refuge and though I often felt out of place (short hair and shaven amongst the retrograde hippies and their wannabees, a Rolex instead of a nose ring, loading my boxes into a sports car instead of a van), I felt comfortably secure in my credentials as lacto-vegetarian and nearly-always-organic-consumer. I was, happily, a card carrying member of the food store, eligible for a five percent discount on purchases made before noon, and a willing contributor to the Forest Fund's five-cents-per-new-bag assessment. Perhaps because I'd spent the "sixties" part of the 1960s in a military uniform, I was fascinated with the time-warped ambiance of the store. The sixties had passed me by, but now I was catching up. I enjoyed the pile of big dogs tied to the small tree in front of the food store, dogs who were invariably pleasant, almost high. I was fascinated by the greetings of friends meeting in the aisles who would merge with each other in interminable hugs; hugs which lasted so long I could shop three sections and a dairy case while they clung silently to each other, slowly rubbing backs, eyes closed, smiling blissfully. The food store was referred to as the "co-op," although it was technically not a cooperative. And I am describing the old store which in the fall of '93 gave way to a new store, bigger, shinier, and an even more pleasant place to shop. The old store, though, had an attitude. It was a mixture of "this store is primarily a place for employees who are often lesbians" and "sometimes the customer is always right." There was a mixed message. But it didn't matter too much to me. My biggest complaint was having to bag my own groceries—and hairy female legs. I proudly retained certain middle-class predispositions. Hairy-legged women were not attractive. Neither were women with beards. Armpit hair was all right with me, though. I wasn't completely rigid.

We ate lots of pasta, lots of tofu, and lots of burritos. We always ate at home, as Linda didn't feel up to going out. She wouldn't eat much at all. Certain foods became disgusting to her. All food odors were vile and upset her. Vegetables like broccoli and cabbage, which had always been her favorites, now turned her stomach. Her appetite was on the wane. She craved sugary stuff, so I wouldn't let it in the house. When I caved in to her junk food cravings and bought it for her, the junk food didn't taste good. She seemed to be living on saltine crackers. Occasionally, she would display a burst of appetite and eat something.

One day, after sending her stool sample, Dr. Jordan announced that she was suffering from a "massive fungus." The diagnosis was Candida albicans just as my brother, the chiropractor, had suggested six months previously. Dr. Jordan immediately prescribed Nystatin. At the drug store, the pharmacist took a large can off the shelf, scooped out some yellowish powder, weighed it, and scraped the excess back into the can. Linda was to take small amounts in water, several times a day. The Nystatin, which has been in use for thirty years, would work to kill Candida albicans located in the gut. With the anti-fungal medication came a strict diet which involved avoidance of sugars and yeasts. Nystatin is nontoxic; it can be used on infants. The only side effect is the dreaded Herxheimer's reaction. Nystatin kills yeast cells brutally, releasing toxins which produce a reaction. Linda became violently ill. It was difficult to convince her to take the Nystatin cocktails which were not at all tasty to the palate. She was glad to finally have a diagnosis but loathed the medicine for the discomfort it brought. The "die off" continued for a long period but she stuck with the medicine, occasionally visiting Dr. Jordan for an intravenous feeding of his special vitamin mixture. Nearly every time she went, he asked her if she had cried about her illness. She didn't like that question. She was also distraught that she was not feeling more well.

Diane Taudvin, Linda's massage therapist, suggested acupuncture and Chinese herbs and recommended a local acupuncturist, Lars Pederson. She told Linda that Lars was a herbalist who customized mixtures for his clients and adjusted the mixture on a weekly basis and that he was inexpensive. I made an appointment for her but she didn't feel well enough and we canceled. Finally, at the end of March she decided to see Lars.

Linda was losing confidence in Dr. Jordan. She was irritated by his questions about her crying. He confused her. She was a good crier. She could cry all the time. She could cry at TV commercials. Linda did not feel that crying was the issue. She should have told him so. Perhaps he was trying to provoke her to an outburst but that wasn't her style. She could cry, sob even, but she wouldn't get in a doctor's face. Too nice. If she was angry at anyone, she hollered at me. I was her universal punching bag. She was also concerned about her liver. It was an intuition thing. She sensed her liver was not functioning properly. This thought came from inside, I suppose; it may have come from her massage therapist who suggested she begin using milk thistle extract, an herbal extract which supposedly helps detoxify the liver.

The liver, we discovered with some research, is a remarkable organ, a chemical laboratory producing over a thousand different enzymes used to digest and assimilate nutrients. It is also a waste treatment plant that cleans toxins from the blood and attacks foreign substances like antibiotics, treats them as poisonous, and eliminates them by releasing them as bile. A toxic condition which continues over a period of time can overwork the liver, exhausting it, making it susceptible to illness such as chronic fatigue, allergies, hepatitis, and immune disorders. In *The Yeast Syndrome* we had read that if Nystatin did not work against Candida albicans, Nysoral was often used. Because she wasn't progressing on Nystatin, Dr. Jordan prescribed Nysoral. Linda did not want to take Nysoral because she had read in Trowbridge's book that it could adversely affect the liver.

I wanted her to follow doctor's orders and bullied her into taking the drug. She put up with it for five days, then quit, refusing to take any more. And the Nystatin did not seem to do anything except make her feel worse.

Chapter 5
Crossing Over

It was at this point, in the early spring of 1993, having finished Thoreau, that I began to get seriously interested in the topic of health. I no longer was prepared to delegate this part of our lives to medical people. We had discovered through our illness, and it had become as much mine as hers, that health is a topic of profound interest to many people. The focus of this interest is one's own health. Interest in the health of others is directly proportional to the state of our own condition. We would not be interested in heart disease, for example, unless we had heart disease or, because of family history, believed there was a possibility we might succumb to heart disease. We are even less interested in rarer ailments like multiple sclerosis or Lou Gehrig's disease. These are lottery-type diseases. Someone else will pull that ticket. Cancer is of interest to all of us because it is pervasive. Breast cancer will catch the attention of all women. Everyone is curious about theories involving colds or flu.

How do we learn about health? Each of us has our own specific experience based on our personal medical history and the histories of family members. Schools teach virtually nothing about health, the history of medicine, nutrition, or public health issues. The primary source of information is the media. Major newspapers and television networks have medical reporters and feed us a steady, if not comprehensive, diet of stories of medical interest. Each of the major networks has an attractive medical doctor who appears on the nightly news and, more frequently, on the morning shows with stories on health issues: skin cancer, breast cancer, new drugs, anorexia, AIDs, birth control, new surgical procedures, organ transplants, diets, mammography, chemotherapy, physical therapy, plastic surgery, health insurance, epidemics, and more. Thus, we are introduced to the female condom, for example, by Katie Couric on "The Today Show," who is holding one in front of the camera and staring at it with an expression of disbelief.

Significant articles from the top medical journals are reported on the evening news and in major newspapers and magazines. Surgical miracles such as the transplanting of an organ or the reattachment of a limb, arm, leg, finger, or penis are universally reported. New surgical techniques such as heart transplants, angioplasty, or bone marrow transplants are highlighted with diagrams in *USA Today*. Seriously ill children with no insurance who need specialized treatment are featured in local newspapers, with encouragements to contribute to their medical fund through rummage sales or other benefits. Medical doctors show up as regulars on local news broadcasts to answer questions sent in by the viewing audience about male pattern baldness, sterility, and psoriasis. Talk radio has doctors—medical doctors—dishing out their world view daily for hours at a time. Drug companies advertise constantly with elaborate television campaigns pushing both "over the counter" and prescription drugs.

Thus, through a media mosaic we receive a constant barrage of information about mainstream medicine and its developments, studies, successes, and occasionally, failures. To our doors come representatives from the Heart Association, Cancer Society, Lung Association, and others, medical research foundations who for years have collected untold amounts of money to conduct research into the more universally feared diseases such as polio, heart disease, cancer, and now the dreaded AIDS. Supermarket tabloids scream about "New Virus Worse Than AIDS" and "Extraterrestrial diseases for which there is no cure." We do get much health news but 95 percent of it is spun from the orbit of hospital-based medicine and the pharmaceutical industry.

The only non-mainstream healers who are allowed on television are the parade of psychologists, who much like economists, can't agree on anything and prattle endlessly about attention deficit disorder, multiple personality syndrome, schizophrenia, eating disorders, depression, self-esteem, empowerment, and dream analysis. To find information about alternative therapies one has to leave the networks, the major newspapers and magazines, the local newspapers, and television shows and search through the information networks which exist to provide data on nontraditional healing arts.

If "The Today Show" does a report on alternative medicine, it will be done by a medical doctor who will overtly or covertly debunk the other healing or medical techniques under investigation. Our primary sources of information have no interest in educating us to use a broad spectrum of healing techniques and, although TV news magazines such as "20/20" will frequently beat up on rogue doctors, and reports will be done on congressional investigations into drug companies' price-gouging practices, the treatment of the medical establishment is generally favorable and leaves one with the distinct impression that it is the only medical system in the world that could possibly do anyone any good. We are captives of our culture, and our culture honors hospital-based medicine and the pharmaceutical industry. These two institutions are reinforced by the medical insurance industry, who will pay for these establishment services and very little else. Physicians practicing standard medicine predominate and pharmacies abound. Hospitals are a source of civic pride in every community where one exists.

Thus, learning about other ways to become healthy besides taking a pill can be a laborious and expensive experience. The body is a vastly complicated mechanism. It seems impossible that a lay person could learn enough to be helpful in identifying causes and solutions to illness.

Linda and I were losing all confidence in the medical establishment. We had harbored doubts about them because of their lack of a position on nutrition. And, medical doctors bad-mouthed chiropractors. Yet our own experience told us that, in certain cases, chiropractors could make one's back well and that diet was important. Therefore, it was no great leap to decide to experiment with acupuncture. Acupuncture, had, after all, since Nixon's trip to China, been looked at with less skepticism than other alternative techniques.

Linda had personally reached a point where she wanted to experiment. She was living in a personal hell of pain and confusion. She was frightened about her condition, entertaining the idea that she was dying a slow death of some horrible disease unknown to science. Physical weakness made it difficult for her to fight back mentally. Pain and unwellness eroded her emotional defenses. She cried like an infant who does not know how to tell you what is wrong.

Lars Pederson was as pleasant as a man could be. He acted pleased that we had decided to come to his small, unpretentious office located in an unremarkable one-story office building between an insurance agent and a travel agency. Lars's wife was the receptionist and office assistant. I sat alone in the waiting room while Lars took Linda to an examination room. In the office a bookcase was filled with books on acupuncture and herbs.

I picked a book at random from the shelf. The acupuncture book had a chapter on eyes, which surprised me. I had been searching through indices and tables of contents in book after book for information on eyes. There was no information which was helpful. In the acupuncture book were several pages of diagrams and descriptions of eye ailments and letter/number codes which I assumed were the various points to place needles.

In another book I read that acupuncture was the primary form of therapy in China (contrasted with the U.S. where drugs are the primary therapy). The Chinese doctor uses several diagnostic techniques: examining the tongue, the eyes, and checking the pulse. Supposedly a Chinese doctor can read the condition of six organs on each wrist by checking the pulse. I read that energy flows through the body following pathways called meridians. These energy rivers flow in the same channels, nourishing all the organs of the body. Chinese medical theory postulates that illness begins when these channels become blocked or imbalanced. Tissues and organs receive reduced energy and cannot do their job. Toxins accumulate and the body manifests disease. The acupuncturist uses needles to eliminate blockages by redirecting energy. The needles can attract or repel this energy which the Chinese call qi or ch'i. Ch'i (chee) is the life force which permeates our world; thus an inexhaustible supply is available to be pulled into the body through the needle antennas or expelled in cases where energy is excessive.

Acupuncture raises some interesting questions for a U.S. citizen. How can hundreds of millions of Chinese survive in sometimes third-world conditions, with ancient sanitation systems and water of questionable quality without the benefit of, and access to, Western Medicine? Most of us know little of China but I'm certain that, from photos and films, we have a general impression of slim, healthy-looking people. We don't associate China with poor health or pestilence. Is it possible that their system of health care works? Is it conceivable that Chinese medicine could work in the United

States or on individuals in the United States? Is there reason to believe Chinese medicine could be equal to, or better than, the medical science which has developed in our country?

The United States is extremely provincial in outlook. It is protected by oceans on the east and west, and the prevailing belief is that Mexico and Canada have little to offer besides vacation destinations, We truly believe we are the greatest country on earth and in the history of the world. The patriotic mantra of the 4th of July and political campaigns put us in the mood of a stadium crowd chanting mindlessly, "We are number one." This credo is simplistically extended to every endeavor and thus we accept, without any investigation or alternative experience, that our educational, political, medical, industrial, social, athletic, or medical systems, though always in need of improvement, are better than, or in the end will prevail over, those of the Germans, the Indians, the Russians, the Chinese, or the Japanese.

As a result of our cultural superiority, most Americans would not be willing to scrap our medical system for that of the Chinese. Our system is better because the Chinese system is. . .well, it's Chinese. Very few Americans could conceive of depending entirely on acupuncture and herbs for their medical care. Yet millions of Chinese get well with Chinese medicine.

If you get the feeling that this is leading up to a proclamation that acupuncture cured all our ills—sorry, it didn't happen that way. Linda, however, was encouraged and excited by this treatment. Lars believed, as did Linda, that the eye was swollen as a result of a spider bite. He had experienced a spider bite himself when he was in acupuncture school. He told her of his experience. Bitten on the thigh, his upper leg had swollen dramatically in the area of the bite. Linda's eye was grossly swollen. It was ugly. Lars's bite had turned an angry red. Linda's eye was red. Her eyeball was still okay. (When I describe her eye I am referring to the tissue around the eye socket including the eyelid.) By this time, the tissue below the eye and slightly above her cheekbone was grossly swollen and red. Lars's bite had stayed angry looking for several months. Linda's eye had been swollen for five months.

At the end of the first session Lars and his wife began taking herbs from glass jars and weighing them on a set of old gold-dust-type scales. Lars selected eight or nine different herbs, or dried flowers, or twigs or pieces of bark, and after measuring them out, wrapped them in a piece of paper and placed that in a brown paper sack. He then repeated the process two more times giving Linda three doses of the herbs and instructions for preparation. The concoction was to be boiled in a nonmetallic pot. Each dose of herbs was good for two days. On the first day the herbs were to be boiled in two and one-half cups of water until only one cup of water was left. The mixture remaining was a thick tea with a powerful odor and taste. The prescription was half a cup morning and night on an empty stomach. The next day the same process was followed, and for several months our one gallon cooking pot held the ever-changing assortment of herbs which Lars selected from the glass jars.

Linda was enthusiastic about acupuncture and herbs, feeling it was "doing something" and from the end of March through the middle of July had two acupuncture treatments a week—a total of twenty-nine treatments, with a cup of rich Chinese herbal soup each day. She was especially pleased when Lars, on her third or fourth visit, put needles directly into the swollen tissue around the eyeball, for Linda had an immense desire to lance the swelling, pop it and, empty it of its contents. We joked that the spider was using her eye as a nest and that the swelling was caused by millions of tiny eggs. The sterile, disposable needles were so thin that Linda often did not feel them, and she would leave an acupuncture session feeling calm and relaxed.

The Chinese approach to medicine was reassuring and made sense. Whereas Western Medicine concentrated on therapies which substituted for the bodies' natural healing powers, the Chinese approach preferred to concentrate on prevention. Prevention is almost unknown in Western medical practice, but in China the doctor's job was to keep families healthy; if they became ill it was considered to be the doctor's fault for not properly diagnosing internal imbalances and moving to restore these systems to balance. In Western Medicine the doctor does not prevent but intervenes after disease appears and, using drugs, creates a stronger force to suppress the intruding disease, creating a substitute for the body's own natural defenses. The Chinese system was slightly contemptuous of a method which tried to close the barn door after the horse had already escaped. Western Medicine believes that disease is essentially a mechanical problem. Something from the outside, a germ, enters the body and causes unwellness. The Chinese view is organic. Energies out of balance allow disease to manifest. For the Chinese doctor, nutrition, exercise, and breathing are considered essential elements in the maintenance of health. Herbs are good and food is medicine. Our own folk saying, "You are what you eat," illustrates this point of view and hints there was a time when we better understood the importance of food in the diet. Dr. Bernard Jensen, emphasizing the importance of natural foods and the necessity to spend more to get good food says, "Spend it on food now or spend it later on the doctors." If our own doctors believed that food was medicine, would the health of the nation be impacted in a positive way?

After a few treatments Linda began to experience a Herxheimer-type reaction. She began to feel sicker and rashes broke out on her back and chest. Lars believed this was a release of toxins and that it was a sign that poisons were moving out of the eye. We were encouraged and continued the twice-per-week treatments through the spring and early summer. She was still taking Nystatin and seemed to be making progress on it. She visited Dr. Jordon, who now began to hypothesize that because of the soreness in her cheekbone, there was a problem involving the root-canaled tooth which remained there. He encouraged us again to find out specifically what kind of substance was used to pack the root. When Dr. Vernon, the endodontist who had operated on the abscessed root canal redid the root canal, he told us he had used a different substance from that used in the original procedure. We asked our dentist to send for the records which showed only that the same type of mercury amalgam was used both times. Dr. Jordon encouraged pulling the tooth, but our local dentist felt the tooth was sound and could be saved. We visited an oral surgeon in Medford, who also believed the tooth was "just fine" and didn't need to be pulled.

As the good weather of summer arrived, Linda seemed to be getting sicker and sicker.

There is a kind of despair that hovers over the chronically ill— a helicopter of confusion pulsating manic energy which alternates between extreme pessimism and mild optimism. When there is sickness in the house, friends and relatives tread carefully and "How's Linda feeling?" soon became a question that I expected but dreaded. Everyone was concerned and suggestions began to come in from all the compass points, each trying to help, each trying to propose the solution. Since the object of our attention was still a spider bite, the solutions offered were directed toward the eye, the swelling, and the inflammation. I would tell the story over and over, adding and subtracting details as we moved along the medical pathway, finding it necessary to offer my own encouragement to our friends and relatives.

One good friend provided a news article about the "aggressive house spider which bites with little provocation." It was described as "relatively large with long hairy legs, possessing necrotic venom, common midsummer to fall. The spider is most aggressive when in search of a mate. Though it rarely bites, the bite results in localized wounds which are slow to heal." Linda read this article over and over.

The spider bite anecdotes poured in as did the antidotes. "Make a compress of cool organic cucumbers or potatoes. Hold it directly on the swelling." "Wash your eye out with Eyebright,"—an herbal remedy. "Use Golden Seal"—another herb. "Hot packs," said one. "Cold packs," recommended another. "Aloe vera gel," suggested the dentist. "Green clay." "Vitamin A ointment." "Lots of vitamin C." "Positive energy flow through visualization." "Art therapy." "Press wet herbal tea bags on your eye."

A physician friend's wife suggested the Mayo Clinic, the nuclear bomb of medicine. Linda's mother recommended the Mayo Clinic, Scottsdale Branch, which was five miles from her home. We could visit while we got well. My mother-in-law, who had moved to Arizona because of a chronic illness and who was now feeling much better, had long predicted that Linda would succumb to heredity and manifest one of the family illnesses like her own fribromyalgia and chronic fatigue syndrome or her father's sister's multiple sclerosis. This expectation greatly upset Linda to the point where the phrase "chronic fatigue syndrome" could not be mentioned in our home. Like many older Americans, Linda's parents seemed to make doctoring a vocation in retirement, although illness for Linda's mother had been an intermittent life-long problem. She had had dozens of surgeries including an early hysterectomy and sectioning of her intestines. Thanks to Medicare and other insurance, very little of their expense was out of pocket, an encouragement to keep going. Our own expenses were now beginning to fall in the out-of-pocket column. Acupuncture was not covered. Neither was massage. Linda wasn't interested in her mother's theories of genetic involvement and avoided talking to her, irritated by mom's co-conspiratorial attitude that they were on the verge of sharing a disease. "You should go ahead and join a chronic fatigue syndrome support group," her mother told her one day. "It's a spider bite, mother," replied Linda.

The eye had been swollen for months now to a point where it looked like it could explode. She couldn't see because the flesh above and below the eye socket had expanded to close the eye. In the corner of the eye socket was a huge bulge, an engorged balloon of skin which fell like a fat man's belly and rested on the puffy skin below the eye. Sometimes the swelling would subside a bit in the evening after she had been up for awhile. But in the morning she always looked like the loser of a fist fight. The right eye, the eye you could still see, looked weak and tired and very sad.

"It's a spider bite," she said. "They are very slow to heal."

A friend told her about a book called *Medicine Cards*. Linda sent me to get it. The medicine cards were like an Indian shaman's version of the tarot. I didn't know much about the tarot but the medicine cards looked less complicated. They were a new age version of a meeting with the tribal elders. In olden times one would draw symbols of animals from a deerskin pouch, and an elder would interpret the "medicine" defined as anything which improves one's connection to the Great Mystery and to all of life. It was a method of devination, a way to make contact with one's animal spirit teachers. We needed a method of devination. The book even suggested that one could call on the medicine of an animal in time of specific need. One of the cards Linda drew was The Spider.

There is a very clear symbology in the idea of spider. The weaving, the web, the venom, the shape. "Spider is the symbol for the infinite possibilities of creation. . .Spider weaves the webs of fate for those who get caught up in her web. . .This is similar to humans who get caught in the web of illusion in the physical world and never see. . .into the other dimensions." Linda read *Medicine Cards* over and over trying to find the secrets they contained.

Massage was becoming an important part of our routine. She would see Diane almost weekly for a professional job, and I would work on her a couple of times a day. Massage was supposed to be vital in the healing process. Good circulation is imperative for optimal digestion and removal of toxins. Poor circulation, I read, can inhibit the body's ability to cleanse itself of its accumulated toxicity. Massage therapy is a proven method of helping to improve circulation. Massage therapists believe they practice a healing art. Through skillful manipulation of muscles beyond the point of tension, massage stimulates lymphatic flow and accelerates removal of lactic acid and other wastes. Synovial fluid which surrounds and lubricates the joints is stimulated by massage. Besides, it is nice to have someone with healing hands put good energy into one's muscles and pull the bad energy out. Linda was always uplifted by her sessions with Diane and believed they were of great benefit in relieving her pain and releasing bad energy. She described these energy releases to me as electricity rushing down her legs or up her spine and out of her body. The massages were, at the least, a consolation and temporary relief from headaches, joint pains, muscle aches, and fevers, for the soreness in her cheek, the sticky eye, the stiff lower back, and the sharp pain in her side.

The only problem was that two acupuncture treatments at $35 each and one massage at $45 was costing $115 per week, or almost $450 per month—not covered by medical insurance because the medical insurance industry, ruled by the AMA and the pharmaceutical industry, does not value acupuncture or massage as healing arts. "You're going to have to pick one for awhile," I said. She picked acupuncture.

In April Linda had a liver screen requested by Dr. Jordan. He called her a few days after the test to report that her liver enzymes were still high.

"What does that mean?" she asked.

"I'm not sure," replied Dr. Jordan.

She worried continuously about her liver. Lars tried to reassure her that it wasn't so unusual, that the liver had lots of work to do and it might take six months to see a change. She shouldn't be overly concerned. He picked out more herbs for the liver.

In addition to liver stress, another stressful situation loomed on the summer horizon. Our son, Noble, and his intended were getting married. Nontraditionally, they were to be wed at our place. In fact, they had decided to have the ceremony in our backyard. Planning was under way. It was to be a small celebration, but even a small wedding is involved. Relatives were all out of state.

Accommodations had to be arranged. The set needed to be designed. Clothing, cake, flowers, food, furniture, decoration, minister, invitations, music, honeymoon were all under discussion. Only sixty people were coming but Linda wanted it to be great. She rose to the occasion, mining the depths of her energy bank. I tried to be cooperative. I helped Noble lay flagstones for a wedding platform on the upper terrace of our backyard. Linda found a picnic table and we talked the seller into delivering it. We located a man who built redwood furniture and ordered Adirondack chairs and benches. Then we contracted with him to build a fence. Linda and I repainted the rockers on the front porch. We painted her aunt's old wooden lawn furniture. I refinished the dining room chairs. We went to the nursery and hauled back boxes of impatiens, begonias, geraniums, scotch moss, and corsican mint. Our friend Lynn volunteered to arrange food. We borrowed a punch bowl. I washed the windows. The kids helped me wash down the back of the house. Linda looked for fabric. She didn't like our shed and wanted to drape it in the style of the artist Christo. We organized a Hawaiian honeymoon.

Summers are warm in Ashland, and the heat softened Linda's aches and pains. She slept late, then got up and tried to supervise all of us, turning all the details over and over on the rotisserie of her mind. She hated the idea that she would look bad at the wedding. Her eye was still swollen and red. She wore dark glasses constantly. Her jaw began to hurt even worse, and she sensed that the root-canaled molar was abscessed again. She didn't want to pull it because it would leave a noticeable gap when she smiled. Filling the gap would be a complicated and expensive dental procedure. But as the wedding date approached, the discomfort increased. It seemed to her a choice between ugly or sick. She wanted to be on her feet for the final preparations and for the wedding itself. She decided to have the tooth pulled and the week before the kid's wedding day we went back to the dentist's office. I sat in the waiting room and drank a cup of coffee. I could hear him arguing with Linda about the tooth. I could tell she was adamant. Even after administering the pain killer, he was trying to convince her the tooth was still healthy. The X-rays showed no infection. The oral surgeon had concurred. "Pull it," I heard her say.

There was silence for several minutes. Then the dentist said, "I'll be darned. You were right. It was abscessed."

Linda sat up that night with a draining gum trying to avoid the dreaded dry socket. Then she rested a few days but was feeling unwell.

"I think maybe I should get an antibiotic," she told me.

"I don't think so." I said. "You've worked too hard to get rid of the candida."

"Something is pulling me down," she argued. "My face is hot. I think I have an infection. I'm going to call someone."

"Antibiotics have only made you sick," I pleaded. But she called the dentist and he prescribed Ery-Tab.

On the day of the wedding the weather was threatening but our crew of relations and friends dressed in shorts and dungarees attacked the backyard with flowers and vases, tablecloths and draperies, Christmas lights, and Japanese lanterns. Auntie Carol and Uncle Fred set up a canopy on the patio to protect the food. Kendra, the bride, and her sister Mia strung lights and hung lanterns. Kendra's mother Jane sewed wedding clothes. Like a time-lapse photo the backyard was transformed into a flowery wedding chapel, more beautiful than any of us could have imagined—except for Linda who had envisioned it all between her naps and her agonies. Our tiny yard, always pretty had become magical, enthralling.

At 5:00 P.M. the weather began to settle. Cakes and food dropped off by friends had been placed on lace tablecloths. Soon the guests began to wander in until the yard seemed crowded. We all milled about in casual clothes, visiting and enjoying the view, relieved that the wind had stopped, waiting for the bride and groom. They appeared, promptly at six, barefoot, and walked quietly past their smiling friends and relatives to the tiled platform where they were joined.

Later, everyone sat on quilts on the grass or on the Adirondack chairs, or on Linda's aunt's old furniture or at the picnic table, or on the new redwood benches and ate the food and cake our friends had brought and watched the light fade, fascinated by the Japanese lanterns and Christmas lights.

Linda, very happily, survived the day but when it was all over she too began to fade very quickly.

Chapter 6
Hydrotherapy

The kids were off to Hawaii. Relatives got into cars and airplanes and left town. Linda was in bed. I walked around the backyard picking up odds and ends of debris and feeling very discouraged. The tooth which we suspected had been causing the problem was out. Now a few days later, Linda was feeling much worse. She told me that her whole body felt like it was swelling up. We had (and I know this is redundant) seen twelve medical doctors, a dentist, an oral surgeon, a massage therapist, and an acupuncturist. Linda had taken Amoxicillin, Tetracycline, Keflex, Lorabid, Prednisone, Atarax, Noroxin, Nystatin, and Erytab and gallons of Chinese herbal tea, yet she was sicker than ever from ailments no one could clearly identify.

It was a mystifying and depressing situation. A chronic illness was a new experience for us. It was humbling. I had thought this would be another self-limiting illness. I had been very wrong. We had done everything right, or so we thought. We had embraced the correct diet, ate low fat and high fiber, drank filtered water, bought mostly organic food, exercised regularly, managed stress, lived in an environmentally safe area, and breathed clean air. We did not drink liquor, smoke tobacco, or use nonprescription drugs. We were behaviorally correct. It did not seem logical that Linda should experience such difficulty.

There had to be an answer. Someone in the world had to have the knowledge to diagnose the cause of her maladies and provide us with a cure. The problem was getting that information.

Two weeks before the wedding Linda had seen Dr. Jordan for the last time. Her liver enzymes were still high. Dr. Jordan then surprised us by suggesting that Linda see an internist. Dr. Jordan, who had seemed so promising and who had clearly helped some very sick people, was throwing in the towel; he was going for the handoff.

Two days after the wedding, Linda was miserable and distraught. She stopped taking the antibiotic (Ery-Tab).

"I'm all swollen," she said, pushing down on her flesh in different places. "And I'm getting red marks all over."

I didn't know what to do. But some action had to be taken. It simply was not acceptable to do nothing. "It's auto-self-intoxication," she said. "It's in Doctor Jensen's book. I'm being poisoned by my own body."

I was not coming up with any good solutions.

"We could try to see the naturopath in Medford," I said.

"That takes a month," said Linda. "I've got to do something right away. I need to get the poison out."

She had heard about a colonic therapist from several friends. Linda called Renee Scherling, who was concerned about Linda's description of her condition. Renee told her to immediately get into a hot bath with Epsom salts and to report to her clinic in the morning. I rushed to Safeway for Epsom salts and dumped a half-gallon into the tub. The bath calmed her for the evening.

In the morning we drove to Renee's house, which was near the hospital. A sign on the front door asked us to take off our shoes. I decided to leave and come back. In an hour, I returned, carefully removed my shoes, and walked into the living room, empty except for a small dog who ran in and jumped up on the couch with me. The living room was the waiting room. The downstairs bedrooms and bath were the treatment rooms. Renee, who apparently lived upstairs, entered the room and stared at me. I noticed she was barefoot.

"You look just like a good friend of mine," she said. "I thought you were him." She handed me a book. "I'm leaving for a week, but you should read this. When I get back, we've got to really work on Linda. I'm very worried about her. She's quite toxic. We moved some shit today," she said laughing loudly. "But she needs cleaning out." Linda appeared, smiling, clearly happy she had found Renee.

"Oh Linda," she said as if Linda was her oldest and dearest acquaintance, "I'm sorry I have to leave but I promised my daughter I'd meet her at Mt. Shasta for the sweat lodge ceremony. I've got to be there. But you hang on until we get back and then we'll go to work." She nodded towards me, "Randy will make soup, fresh soup for you every day that I'm gone. Eat the soup, drink the broth. You can have some fresh juice, some watermelon, lots of watermelon, but nothing else. We've got to start the cleanse. Take an enema if you need to. Keep your bowels moving. You need to consider going to Optimum Health."

I gave Renee a check for $55. She gave me a brochure on the Optimum Health Institute of San Diego, California, and a recipe for vegetable soup plus a book on oxygen therapy. It was a whirlwind visit and, blasted with Renee's high energy, we walked to the car which was very hot from sitting in the sun.

"Well?" I asked.

"Oh, she's just great," said Linda. "She's a healer. She knows."

"Did you have a colonic?"

"Oh boy. Did I ever! It was unbelievable. I feel better."

"If you feel better," I said, "it's worth it."

I drove to our next stop which was Diane's for a massage. "Listen," I said. "You might have to consider dropping acupuncture for awhile. We've given it a good shot, and it doesn't seem to be solving your particular problem."

"I think it's good," she said.

"I do too; but we can't do everything. This is all getting very expensive."

Later, Linda called Lars and told him she was going to undergo some colonics and thanked him for his help. He warned her that colonics could sap her energy. We never heard from Lars again.

Every day for the next two weeks I went to the store and bought organic onions, beets, carrots, and potatoes, sliced them thinly and made a clear broth vegetable soup in an amount small enough so that there would be none left over.

When Renee returned from the sweat lodge, Linda had two series of colonics—a total of eight in addition to the one she had before Renee left on her trip. After the fourth or fifth one Linda started talking about tapeworms. This sent me back to the library to look for information on worms. There wasn't much but I did find a drawing of a tapeworm. The picture showed that they were ribbon-like and segmented with a small head. The book said they could grow to significant length.

LINDA'S VOICE: *Tuesday—lots of pain in my side—deep breaths—worked through it. Hard, dark things—stringy stuff and sludge. Red flushed face—like a fever when passing toxins. Tuesday night—*

deep aching all over—woke around 3:00 A.M. and drank lots of water. Randy rubbed my back. Went back to sleep. Woke on Wednesday. Really stiff hands, wrists, and ankles. Took a hot bath. Back to Renee's for another colonic—pieces of stuff that looked like tissue. Toxic looking liquid—yellow. Deep stomach massage from Renee. "Let's go after it," she said—pour the water—breathe deep—lots of pain—masses passing—like tissue—light and dark. Can really feel it moving—unlocking—moving through. Renee holds mirror down so I can see. Fish tail. Too much, too big to pass. She says you'd better get up quick and go to the toilet. I'm weak—can hardly move—put a tissue under my butt and go to bathroom—sit down with head in hands, push just a little and feel huge release—sort of a wriggling—I got up—we check the toilet—she's poking it with a stick and holding me up with her other arm. I'm saying "Oh my gosh" and trying not to scream in shock. Three feet long! All one piece. HUGE! Hard, dark, just like Dr. Jensen's book—unbelieveable—a horror story—I'm in shock.

From colonic number seven, Linda brought home a souvenir—a plastic bag containing what she and Renee alleged was a tapeworm. It was ribbon-like and had what looked to be a head. But I couldn't see any segments so I wasn't so sure. Linda, however, was convinced she had tapeworms.

"That's why Renee thinks I should go to the Optimum Health Institute. They use wheatgrass juice to kill all the parasites in your system. I think I'd like to go," she said.

The Optimum Health Institute offered one, two, and three- week sessions. The Institute's brochure promised, ". . .an advanced concept in alternative health education." They recommended a three-week course during which one would discover how to cleanse the body of toxins with living foods. According to the brochure, the OHI folks believed that "the human body is self-regenerating and self-cleansing and, if given the proper tools with which to work, it (the body) can maintain its natural state of well-being." "Tuition" for three weeks in a standard private room was $1,425. This fee included room, meals, class instruction, linen, and use of the wheatgrass juicer. Colonics, massage, chiropractic, and book were extra. The diet at The Optimum Health Institute consisted of sprouts, greens, fruits, vegetables, seed sauces, juices, enzyme-rich rejuvelac, sauerkraut, and wheatgrass juice.

I knew something about wheatgrass juice, having been a wheatgrass rancher a couple of years previously. On one of our visits to Hawaii to see my brother, Dr. Bart had insisted we grow wheatgrass and juice it daily. He told me to purchase *The Wheatgrass Book* by wheatgrass guru Ann Wigmore. Ms. Wigmore is the founder of the Hippocrates Health Institute in Boston. OHI was clearly a western cousin. My ranch had been located on a table in our sun room. Plastic trays filled with a mix of peat moss and topsoil were sown with wheat berries soaked overnight. Each tray was covered with another tray turned upside down, creating a miniature greenhouse. Within three to four days the young sprouts of wheatgrass were strong enough to lift the top tray into the air. The lid was removed and four to five days later, grass would be harvested and ground in a grinder, squeezing out an ounce or two of dark green, pungent liquid. The easiest way to drink it was to throw it back in a small glass like a shot of whiskey. The juice packed a punch, and a full shot could make one's eyes blur.

Ann Wigmore and the people at OHI in San Diego clearly believe wheatgrass juice was a panacea. They described it as "the staff of life!" They said that the juice contained Vitamins A, B, C, D, and E, and essential minerals such as calcium, iron, magnesium, phosphorus, potassium, and zinc, plus enzymes and all essential amino acids. Its chlorophyll promotes cleansing and provides nourishment and energy for cells, organs, and tissues.

The brochure pictured happy, healthy people sitting in classes, growing wheatgrass, working in the garden, exercising, and lounging in the large hot tub. The campus was tree-lined and grassy.

Renee had actually been there more than once and said she wanted to go again. It was a vacation for her. A tonic. Linda wanted to go too, to continue her cleanse, to purge her system of toxins and worms—to rejuvenate her cells. With airfare and spending money it would be a $3,000 adventure. Linda's excitement and optimism about the wheatgrass juice program raised her spirits considerably. We needed to do something radical to break her cycle of unwellness. We'd gone to every medical doctor we could think of. They'd given up on us and we had lost faith in them. I made reservations and bought her a plane ticket. I was tired of making soup every day. It would be a good break for me as well. In the meantime, I had been invited by Linda and Renee to witness the colonic process. An honored guest.

I took my shoes off and followed Linda into the house. I waited in the living room until Linda had changed. Renee then called me to come in. I entered a small room. Linda was in a kind of gown and was lying on her side on a massage table. Renee sat on a stool next to the table where she could reach the colonic machine. It was a metallic box with a Plexiglas window in the center, and behind the Plexiglas I could see a tube which crossed horizontally. The tube allowed one to observe the "product" as it flowed by. A flex hose came out of the left side of the machine. I cringed when I saw the plastic tip on the end of the hose. It was ten times bigger than a colema tip. The girls were excited. Linda had been producing trophies. It should be a good show. Renee flipped a switch allowing water, which was under some pressure, to enter the colon. After a minute Linda raised her hand, indicating some slight pain, and Renee let the water to flow out. It bubbled through the tube, which soon began to display items that flashed across my line of sight like salmon past the viewing window at a fish ladder. Lumps and clumps and stringy things. "There's a worm," said Renee, as something long and squiggly floated by. I couldn't be certain it was a worm. There was lots of product but no trophies today. They were kind of disappointed. "You should have come yesterday," said Linda.

Linda was very weak and seemed to be developing a serious chest or lung congestion. In less than a week she was scheduled to fly to San Diego. The colonic regimen had been tiring. Linda had lost some weight, and throughout the course of this illness had also lost muscle mass. She had been living on my vegetable soup. Her formerly athletic-looking body was becoming frail. Her hands were sore and overnight would close like claws, and in the morning she had to soak them in hot water to get them to open up. The joints of her fingers, wrists, and knees were red and swollen.

LINDA'S VOICE: *Up at 3:00 A.M. —hard to breathe (face and eye hurt). Body massage—wrists, hands, chest. Walked in backyard bare feet on ground—moon reaching—light reflecting on my palms—star gazing; beauteous. Warm water/lemon juice/reading. Toxins trying to escape—joints in hands, hips, neck all really sore. Randy made great juice with garlic and some soup. Coughed and coughed up stuff. Took a ginger bath. Sat in sun. Warmth felt good. Took two naps. For three days had gag coughing—finally sticky stuff with small red dots came up. Be strong—take charge—take control of health.*

At night Linda would sweat and her breathing was raspy. She was feverish. She was coughing a dry cough. It was inconceivable to me that she could make it onto an airplane, change planes in San Francisco, and wrestle her bags to a taxi stand at the San Diego Airport. Based on her symptoms, I thought she might have pneumonia. I was worried and very tempted to take her to the emergency room again, But, then, they would only give her more tests and antibiotics which, to this point, had not helped anything.

I called Renee. "Linda is very sick," I said. "I don't think she can make it to Optimum Health. What would you do? Would you go to a medical doctor?"

I had dialed up America Online on my computer and checked its health directory for symptoms of pneumonia. They were fever, muscle aches, fatigue, headaches, cough with small to moderate amounts of sputum and chest pain. Linda had all of the above. I felt a wave of panic. People die from pneumonia. I recapped these symptoms to Renee who had formerly been a nurse.

Renee was cautious. Clearly, as a health professional she didn't want to advise against the medical establishment. She believed that some local doctors were trying to close her down anyway. They had sent undercover people to her clinic for treatment to find out what she did and what she told her clients. This was not so farfetched. We had heard stories of how the Ashland medical community, some years before, had run a holistic physician by the name of Lynn Anderson out of town. This in a community that had a widespread reputation for political and social liberalism and where alternative practitioners—psychics, faith healers, chiropractors, naturopathic, massage therapists were seemingly accepted and welcomed by the community. Renee simply did not know me well enough to tell me not to cave in to the temptation of the quick fix.

"You could see a medical doctor," she said, "And, under these circumstances, I might too. But, why don't you try a naturopath?"

I explained the difficulties we had experienced in trying to get appointments with naturopathic doctors, the endless questionnaires, the long waits for appointments.

"Call Martin Osterhaus," she advised. "He operates a little differently."

It was a long night of coughing, sweating, and aching for Linda. "You don't have to go to San Diego," I told her. "You can stay here."

"I've got to do something to get well," she sobbed. "I think it will help."

It seemed that we had reached a critical and desperate stage in our illness. We had no faith in the prevalent medical system and no real knowledge or understanding of the alternatives. The testimonials from Optimum Health Clinic were encouraging: "Tens of thousands of guests have experienced the benefits of the Optimum Health Program and achieved miraculous results," proclaimed the brochure. We were definitely in the mood for a miracle. But first we had to get Linda on her feet and ready to fly.

I called Dr. Osterhaus on Wednesday morning and gave him a brief overview of the problem. Amazingly, he said he could see us that same afternoon.

Dr. Osterhaus lived in a suburban neighborhood of houses built in the 1950s. Like Renee's, the office was in his home, a one-story ranch with a gravel parking strip next to his concrete driveway. The driveway terminated at the window of the family room, formerly the garage. In the great tradition of ranch-style houses, the garage had been enclosed. Now instead of containing cars, it was the doctor's office, furnished with an exam table, various small medical tools, a desk with shelves for books and—a piano! The living room was the waiting area. When we entered the house, me holding Linda up by the arm, we heard a voice holler. "Be right with you!" Dr. Osterhaus was with a patient.

I liked the set-up immediately. I had judged the book by its cover for too long. After marching through numerous clinics, offices, and hospitals with their expensive, if uncomfortable, furniture, shiny machines, electrically-operated tables, too many employees, color-coded files, rotating filing cabinets, insurance forms, expensive prints, and other objets d'art, it was good to be in somebody's living room waiting for help.

The other car in the driveway had California plates. When Dr. Osterhaus emerged with an elderly couple it was clear from the dialogue they were long-time patients. It seemed to me a good sign they would drive up from California, even if only from Yreka, a forty-five minute drive from Ashland. I didn't know then that naturopaths weren't allowed to practice in California. If a resident of California wanted to see one they had to go to Oregon or some other state.

Dr. Osterhaus was wearing Levi's and moccasins and a silky, loose-fitting shirt. He had a short ponytail pulled tightly back. Slightly built but strong looking, he radiated healthy energy. I liked the rather dowdy living room and was ready to deal with a doctor in moccasins. I didn't care if it turned out to be a costume or a premeditated pose. It was a better, less pretentious, more accessible way of dressing than the uniform of clinic and hospital. By now, I would see an Indian shaman if I knew where one was. We had crossed over.

When entering a clinic or large medical practice or hospital one is invariably faced with the standard office barrier of a counter staffed by the ubiquitously supercilious female who always seems to be the first point of contact in a doctor's domain, handing you a clipboard and a pencil and sending you back to your chair like a bad student in a study hall to fill out the exam and then return it to her to be stuck in a file, never to be read. From the counter to the upholstered chair, then to an exam room, usually without windows, to sit and wait for the great one to appear, dressed in his white cloak. I had experienced exceptions and variations on this theme, but never had I been met at the door of the family room by a smiling doctor in moccasins.

We sat in armchairs and got acquainted. I briefed Osterhaus on our adventures and on Linda's symptoms. I told him of her planned departure for The Optimum Health Institute. He was familiar with the Hippocrates Institute and the wheatgrass juice concept. Although he showed no great enthusiasm for wheatgrass juice, he evidenced no inclination to talk us out of the trip. He sensed Linda's southerly momentum.

"The couple who were just here have been to the Gerson Clinic in Tiajuana," he told us. I had never heard of the Gerson Clinic.

"They treat cancer," he said.

I reiterated my concern about pneumonia. Dr. Osterhaus listened to Linda's lungs with a stethoscope. "The lungs are clear," he said. "We could take a sputum test, but I don't think it's pneumonia. Dr. Jordan was probably right about candida. Candida can create lots of different symptoms. What we need to do is try and jump-start you a bit. Your vitality is very low. Let's see if we can get you in shape to get on an airplane."

He gave her a B-12 shot. He stretched her out on his exam table and gave her an adjustment. His adjustments seemed different from those we had experienced at the hands of chiropractors. The manipulations were more vigorous and he ended by pulling hard on her neck.

"Yikes," she said, "I felt that way down in my lower back."

And on this day and the next two he also gave her hydrotherapy.

Dr. Osterhaus told us that, when he decided to become a doctor, he wanted knowledge that would allow him to help people by using his hands. He had no special equipment, no X-ray machines or other diagnostic equipment.

"I'll make good use of blood tests," he told us. "When you get back we'll get a blood workup. But now we're going to do something very simple. We'll use hot and cold water to get some energy moving. I'll show you how so you can do it at home whenever you feel the need. Water is one of our most therapeutic medicines."

Dr. Osterhaus was clearly a believer in what he called "hydrotherapy," using water to heal. He was also a natural teacher. And while he administered hot and cold towels to Linda's bare chest and back he gave us a short course on hydrotherapy specifically and naturopathy in general.

"Our bodies are mostly water. Just as the moon influences water on the earth, hydrotherapy moves the waters of our bodies in a natural and very powerful way. The movement of fluids acts to cleanse, flush, nourish, stimulate, and heal the body's tissues. It is a very powerful healing technique. By proper application of hot and cold temperatures, I can influence the body's inner fluids to move in a very directed way. The fluids I'm talking about are the blood, lymph, and cellular fluids; we move those fluids toward, away from, or through chosen parts of the body. Hydrotherapy can enhance circulation, promote detoxification, and eliminate waste. A bath, you know, is hydrotherapy. Are you taking baths?" he asked Linda.

"Yes," I answered for her. "She's been taking Epsom salts baths."

"That's good," he said, walking back toward his kitchen, with me trailing behind, to heat another towel. "We just went up into the mountains this weekend and built a sweat lodge. You should drive up there and pick some yarrow and elderberry and make a bath for Linda. It's a wonderful bath. Add some apple cider vinegar and sea salt. It would be very soothing."

"To do hydrotherapy," he continued standing at the sink, "you need three towels—a large, medium, and small. We'll start with Linda on her stomach."

He wrung the hot towel into a tight knot and I followed him back into the family room feverishly writing notes in my small notebook: "three towels, yarrow, elderberry, back first, sea salt."

"We're going to put the big towel on her back for five minutes," he said, opening the towel and spreading it with a dramatic snap. "Then we tuck her in tight with a wool blanket." Linda now looked like a plaid cocoon. We walked back to the kitchen to prepare towel number two.

After five minutes we went to step two. A second hot towel was laid out on towel number one and flipped over. Towel number two was now next to the skin and number one was removed. The blanket was retucked. Linda was starting to purr. It was clear that Dr. Osterhaus expected me to continue this treatment at home.

"Hydrotherapy doesn't cure ailments; the body does that. This, of course, is the basis of naturopathy. The body heals itself and the physician (physician means teacher, you know), the physician helps get the body in balance so the healing process can start. Hydrotherapy can give the body sometimes critical help in healing. It provokes a natural healing process. It can help regulate glandular function and regularize metabolism. It can even mobilize white blood cells and move them to areas where they are needed."

"Are you feeling warm all over?" he asked Linda.

"Oh yes," she said. "It's wonderful."

"Do you feel any air leaks?" he asked, fooling with the blanket.

"No, I'm comfy," she said.

"It's nice to be all tucked in, isn't it?" said Doctor Osterhaus. "Okay. Our ten minutes are almost up. Let's go get a cold towel ready. You'll be surprised how good that feels," he was saying to Linda as he left the room.

The cold towel was placed on the cooling towel number two, then flipped again. "Are you getting a little buzz?" he asked. Linda sighed.

"Relaxing, isn't it? There are some very powerful movements going on in your body but all you feel is cozy, warm, cool, and very relaxed. It's a wonderful therapy. This particular therapy was developed in the nineteenth century by a Trappist monk named Father Kneipp. He understood the almost magic healing properties of water. What we are doing is called 'constitutional hydrotherapy,' but baths, steam, colonics, and alternating temperatures are also hydrotherapy. A shower is hydrotherapy, especially if you take a cold one after a hot one. It's amazing what you can do with just water! Always take a cold shower after a hot one. That gets the body fluids moving."

The information was coming at me in waves. My notes were illegible. I put down my pen and notebook.

"Tell me again about the yarrow. I know yarrow, but I'm not sure of elderberry. Where do I find it?"

"Drive up Dead Indian Road," said Dr. Osterhaus. "When you get to the top you'll see large shrubby trees with white clumpy blossoms. It's in full bloom now. You can't miss it. Take some paper grocery bags. Clip yarrow and elderberry blossoms and mix them up in the bags. Then, boil the two flowers and the yarrow stems in a pot until they are really cooked down. It will turn kind of a brownish yellow. Strain it out and dump it in the bath. Very soothing. A wonderful bath," he said in a very satisfied way.

The next morning, armed with hand pruners and grocery bags, I drove into the mountains. The sky was bright and clear, the air was clean, the highway lined with Indian paintbrush, vetch, and larkspur. At the top, where the mountains leveled off into a plateau, yarrow grew profusely next to elderberry trees which were in full bloom. In thirty minutes I filled six bags with the herbal mix. I sealed the bag tops, as the plants were home to tiny mites, spiders, and ants which were now on their way down the mountain back to Ashland hoping to escape from the brown paper before the flowers were boiled to a brown soup.

LINDA'S VOICE: *Took my special bath; lay in the hammock wrapped in a cotton sheet, sweating and watching the humming-birds fighting over the feeder. Then I saw buzzards circling way above me—went inside—took a nap. Randy played golf. Then Shawn called and they went for a swim at reservoir.*

Linda claimed that the baths were, in fact, very soothing, that hydrotherapy was revitalizing, and that she wanted another one of those B-12 shots before she left on Sunday. Dr. Osterhaus, in my opinion, had performed a minor miracle in three days of hands-on therapy. Linda was packed and ready to travel. But as she passed through the airport X-ray machine wearing a little straw hat, I still wondered if she could make it to San Diego.

Chapter 7
The Wheatgrass Diaries

LINDA'S VOICE: August 15, 1993. I arrived at the Optimum Health Institute around 4:00 P.M., checked in, filled out forms. They fixed me a special lunch—all raw (carrots, radishes, sprouts). Will my teeth hold out? Took a long time to eat—sitting in the sun. Picked up my supplies and paid for room. Tour of grounds by Sam. He's been here with his wife for thirteen years growing organic foods. Showed me the wheatgrass growing rooms and the juicing machines. Saw a video. Learned about Rejuvelac. Had a killerpee. Grabbed food and limped as fast as I could to Room 57 after having paid deposit for alarm clock/phone/towels. Ate four to five different kinds of sprouts in my Room. AAA-type accommodations. Concrete block. Pretty basic but it's (not for profit) clean.

A poor woman just walked over the bridge to upper floors of my building. I'm on ground floor. I've seen her making her solitary, painful way all afternoon. Ten minutes, ten steps. I'll make my painful way, too, I guess.

I'm feeling a little more energized so maybe I'll go to the orientation and see who's here. My knees are really hurting! Hard to walk very far. Room looks pretty good at night. Hands hurt to open door. Miss you guys—but anxious to get on with this program. Good night, love you.

Monday, August 16, 1993. Slept great after a hot bath. I was cold before the bath but went to bed sweating—slept in long johns—window open. Good bed, quiet (up at 6:30 A.M.—tried to meditate). Exercise at 7:30. Brisk walk. Then to juicing room. Lots of talk about expense. Consensus is—reasonable price here compared to back east or clinics in Mexico. Used wheatgrass juice as poultice on bruises/sores. Went to classes. Took notes:

Control of your universe
Ruler of your body

Put aside old habits

The 4 P's

1. Positive mental attitude—visualization.
2. Patience with self.
3. Persistence—relax—take time.
4. Prayer—to higher source—release of problems.

"My Dear, you have to learn to be your own doctor. We're all different," said Ann Wigmore who founded the original wheatgrass institute in Boston.

There's as much wheatgrass (WG) juice as we need. Try and drink a little more each day. Good for poultices. I keep telling them to paint the bathrooms green. The green juice gets all over everything. The enemas and implants (E's & I's) are highly encouraged. The WG juice is supposed to be an antiseptic. Hold the juice in the colon for 20 minutes. Wait an hour. Go get more juice. Sip an ounce. Clean up bathroom with cold water and mild soap.

Felt nauseous after WG poultice on eye. Dipped sore hands in wheatgrass juice—took a nap. Little man is ringing a bell. Guess it's dinner.

Nausea is disappearing. Hope this aversion to WG goes away. Just to smell it makes me want to throw up. I'm very cold. Put on warm layers and go to dinner although I'm not hungry. Most people moving slowly like me. We're the slow motion people. I'm in the right place. My short-term goal is to be able to put my name tag on and squeeze the enema and implant bulb without pain. Dinner—chunky soup—gazpacho, sprouts, and salad. Evening class on "stress." Then affirmations. "Love yourself. Improve yourself." (I wore my denim skirt/red sweater tucked in, denim blouse—white ruffle socks, blue straw hat). Daytime temperatures are comfortable but it's cool in the evening. Nausea gone. Eye, face, joints—very sore. Tomorrow—a massage. Weighed myself today. 135. Somewhere in the last month I've lost 20 pounds. Wow! Didn't realize the cushion of fat, the buffer, protection from the world. Interesting feeling to be in touch with body, with vulnerability. Took a hot bath as usual. Good night. Sleep tight.

Tuesday morning—slept great! Classes. Enemas and implants (E's & I's). WG juice. Massage, chiropractor. Classes. Raw veggies.

Wednesday morning—scheduled early colonic. Had to go to juicing room first to get WG. With colonic can get WG deeper into gut. Learned organs of elimination:

1. Lungs—respiration
2. Skin—perspiration—largest eliminative organ
3. Lymphatic—circulation
4. Kidneys—urination—blood filter
5. Liver—cleans blood
6. Colon—defecation
7. Reproduction—menstruation

Sitting outside room in sun. Little lady from class—who had colon surgery a year ago—talked about WG, cleansers, colonics, acidophilus. At 12:30 did E's & I's. Knees feel better/red sores on hands coming to a head. My short-term goal/be pain-free while turning key in the door. Discovered a big lump on my left forearm. Have a similar lump on left wrist. Sores on hands bright red; painful to write or do almost anything. More WG implanted. Don't think I'll drink any today. I can't stand the taste.

Eighty-year-old lady named Afton gave a long but interesting testimony. We got to lie down on the floor and listen. Listening and learning. Don't feel too tired. Both enemas today expelled worm things. Afton told about her final worm cleansing. After four to six months she passed large mass with worm still in it! Some men are measuring for a new hot tub. The beautiful tub in the brochure doesn't work. People are complaining about that. Geraniums three to four feet tall. Lots of impatiens. The smell of WG everywhere. E's & I's getting a bit easier. Not making such a mess. Couldn't hold WG juice very long today. Maybe need to warm up WG. Inside of nose is really scabby and sore.

What you're feeling is what your body's doing. Caring, sharing people. Safe place.

It's 10:00 P.M.—I'm very sleepy. Took hot bath. Imagine a huge room full of people lying on the floor—talking us into a relaxed state. Very old people. Caring, loving, giving teachers. (I wore my beige shorts and white shirt and hat. Evening—red sweats, red sweater, blue shirt, and shawl). Either it's cold or I'm continuing to really detox. Massage today wasn't so hot—so not going to do that again. Diane has spoiled me. Japanese boy said I was a very good cleaner of the juice room. People are starting to look familiar and talk to each other a little more. Good sweat from bath even after cold shower—but miss my secret ingredients. So hard to get up and down from floor. Hands, wrists, arms, knees, ankles—ouch! I like my little room—feel safe. Although, how would they know if you croaked? I think I'm retracing or have a big tumor in my arm. Looks like a golf ball to me. Put WG poultice on it and eye—eye is looking okay?

Office lady lives nearby—working to help pay for her care—three months (cancer?— really pretty—about 45). It's kind of hard to talk to people without asking "What's wrong?"

Colonic people are very busy—had to take 7:00 A.M. appointment. But I feel I need it. Stuff still coming out. Hard to drink tons of water. Thankful I'm sleeping so well and that the freeway is on the other side of building. My sense of smell is ACUTE. YIKES—the soap I bought has taken on new life—may have to stop using it. A girl was chided for chewing gum. I'm not wearing deodorant. Let that trash escape. Love you for realizing this is what I needed. I was very sick.

Toilets are hard to flush. Have to press the lever down with the handle of my body brush. Don't know if I would recommend this program to many. Have to be pretty sick, desperate, and very dedicated.

Good beds—soak hands—really swollen. Chest clearing up—still tender—not much coughing. Fingers not working well enough for WG implant. Can't squeeze the bulb. Will have to do later.

Maggie, the colonics lady, is a wonderful listener. Said Renee had done a great job. Fascinated by story. Tape worms for sure. She's seen thousands in four years. Never heard such a detailed cleansing. Body was highly toxic. Immune system depleted by drugs. Worms and parasites eating me. The worms lay eggs in gelatinous masses like the last ones I passed. Wheat grass juice cleanses—grabs mucous—pulls it out. Long strings. Feel like I can breathe better. Going to end of exercise class. I'm at the right place.

Drank juice outside in sun. Before meals we form a circle—hands not touching—left hand up receiving—right hand down—giving. People look pretty tired. I told Diana she looked cute in her body suit. She said she felt like shit.

Yesterday I poured leftover WG all over my body and rubbed it in while standing in the shower. Pretty messy. Will have to pay extra for towel cleaning.

The hardest thing is getting up and down off the floor for E's & I's. I'm waiting now to perk up and go make more WG for second implant.

They're having a talent shown on Friday. Can you believe it? Showers and more showers. The tendency is to get green all over. Still have big lumps on hands and fingers but redness and swelling is going away. Continue to soak with WG. Also eye. Put some up nose. But think I'll wait till tomorrow to drink. Old-timer tricks for drinking WG:

1. Take a deep breath and drink without smelling.
2. Suck lemon or orange right after.
3. Dilute.
4. Go slow—build up to it.

Heard outside my window, "I've been to one meeting. It's just not my cup of tea." People are just bad. I'm very good. I've been to *all* the meetings. Now I have to get up and dressed for my dinner juice.

At burning ceremony—lit papers. Stood around in a circle and told what we were grateful for. Sat next to Sheri from Alaska. I like her. She's a three-weeker. I'm really tired. Can't believe tomorrow is Thursday. Try to rest more tomorrow. Feel like I'm being purged. Starting to breathe better.

I got dizzy in the laundry room. Feel like I have a slight fever but knees are going up and downstairs really good. I'm just lying here on my firm bed waiting for 1:30 class. Looking forward to apple soup for dinner. I can see a mall across the freeway. May venture out this weekend. My glasses are broken and pen is drying up.

Debbie Reynolds comes here regularly. Sheri has her room. I think my nose scabs are healing. What causes those? Smells are bothering me. Food smells hit me when I come in back door. Hope it stops smelling icky. Noble called around lunch time. It was so good to hear his voice. He said, "What! You put wheatgrass juice up your butt!" Doesn't sound weird anymore to me.

I'm sucking vitamin B-12's and C's. Taking my acidophilus everyday. Some multivitamins too, but they're hard on my stomach. Not eating much. Just watermelon for breakfast and small juice—green, of course. Glad I'm staying for two weeks. Pretty sure I'll go for three and get my CERTIFICATE—suitable for framing!

I met Larry who was in a wheelchair fifteen years ago when he first came here. Nothing docs could do for him. He had MS, agent orange, etc. He's doing okay. My lymphatic system is starting to flow. My heart is not beating so loudly that I can hear it and feel it. For days I felt it was going to pop. Emotional, weak, achey. It's all good. It's nice to lie here on my back. My neighbor is practicing for the talent show with a strange-looking violin, playing "Turkey in the Straw."

Lunch today was actually delicious—gazpacho with avocado and sprouts, mung beans, asparagus, and a sauerkraut concoction. I have met some very nice people—but, where's Debbie?

Got lots of phone calls today. Randy has been frustrated trying to get through. My phone was out of order. He's in Yakima—playing golf. I'm here pulling worms.

Friday: The talent show was cool—poetry, songs, jokes, musicians, magician, dance, readings, skits—all good and entertaining. Lots of show biz people come here—mainly, I think, to lose weight.

This week really whizzed by. Feeling pretty strong right now. Sweating, sleeping, exercising. E's & I's continue on the weekend. Oh boy. Congratulations to me. I'm a first-weeker.

Saturday: I'm still achey. Skin tone seems better. Try not to look. I sort of gasp when body brushing. But noticed slight red rash on face and chest. Maybe WG—speaking of which, I need to go get juice for E's & I's. I did see Paula in dining room before she left—having a hearty meal of raw sweet corn, sunflower seed sprouts, yummy tomatoes, celery, baby mung beans, and alfalfa sprouts. Funny how you cross paths/connect—sometimes it's just for an instant—a few days. I wonder what her story was. She's been here before—is obviously very ill—kept to herself—said she didn't have the strength to communicate. People take care of her at home. Said this time was harder for her. Hard getting up and down. Told me what a mess she had made in her bathroom—so bad I would be spared the details. Dark hair—a wig, I think. Wanted to say good-bye but then I saw her leaving—walking slowly over the bridge.

Here's what you need for E's & I's: a little plastic bucket, flexible tubing, lubricant, bulb thing, measuring cup for WG, plastic cup, blue plastic sheet, low padded bench. What else? Go do it—go do it—go do it.

Dr. Mark runs the place. His mother, Mrs. Solomon, is currently in Israel teaching people to grow and use "you know what." The WG word. Wheatgrass here I come—you little green blades of hope.

Great visit with Sheri. She's a tomboy. Her boyfriend restores race cars (dragsters) and Sheri's the driver. She has a blond buzz-cut and tons of earrings. When she was 20, she decided she wanted to get away from people. Got in her car and started driving north. At the Canadian border she just kept going. She's been an Alaskan for thirty years and can talk about wolves and caribou. She drives her car 120 mph!

She said the lymph nodes in her neck were the size of marbles but were going down. The swelling in my arm is going down. Fascinating lady. She wants to go to horse races tomorrow. I may pass. Sheri does her bath cleanse wearing a snorkel! Interesting to meet her, as one of my goals is to become more adventuresome. 120 mph! Wow—a healthy feeling. Exciting. I know now I'm going to be okay. Better than okay. Better than ever. New, different—healed in body, mind, and spirit—even if in the morning I'm achey—I'll remember this—a glimpse of things to come. Free, content, happy, strong, positive—120 mph—oh yes!

Sunday: Slept terrific. Last night something changed. Still have a pain occasionally but can breathe easier/smoother/not so out of breath—little coughing—but seems like stuff is flowing—coming up, moving around, nose and eyes aren't so dry. Hard, crusty things in nose are going away.

Ernie's wife Annie is a TV star. She came down to visit him and brought their Yorkshire puppies. Ernie and Annie both wear cowboy boots and lots of black. Annie—I recognized right away from "Evening Shade." She was pleased. So soft-spoken. Ernie's lost twelve pounds.

Took a tour of the rooms after dinner with Sheri, Joyce, Alice, and Diana. We saw the townhouses and deluxe bungalows. What a bunch of characters. They'd all been to the beach. Sheri went wading in her nylons. Pretty rowdy. Alice drove them in her big Mercedes. Lots of people staying second, even third week. Feel good about first week. Making progress with joints, pain in chest, energy, sores on hands. Determined to get well: I'm tired of knowing what it's like to be an invalid—disabled—a captive in your body. I want to dance off this plane of existence.

<u>Monday</u>: 7:30 A.M.—Hot bath to loosen up and I'm out of here. Hello Monday.

Ernie visited with the girls at breakfast then off to sprouting class. Growing wheat grass is cheap—only pennies a day. Doesn't cost a fortune to get healthy. (You just have to turn green first.)

A circle before lunch—outside, holding hands. I'm grateful to be here and to be feeling stronger every day. Coughing up some icky stuff. White, scabby things in my nose are coming out. Red bumps on fingers looking better. Someone said my eye looked less red. Told them I was putting WG on it. "How did you ever think of that?" was their response. People like to joke a lot about WG. Most people don't like it much. Couldn't eat much lunch. Didn't seem too appetizing plus I have another big canker sore—so I'm a little hungry. Been thinking about a baked potato.

I may have to move. The person next door plays loud music. I called office to complain. They asked him to turn it down. Oh well, is it time to leave #57?

Diana from Germany says the "F" word a lot. She's been in the U.S. for two years—excellent English. Does massage and cleaning. Says she's the worst cleaner but people seem to think German girls clean well. She's very busy but says she's the worst cleaner she knows.

Dinner with Sheri. Gazpacho. Talked about guys, old tapes and movies, pierced ears, hair, asbestos, pillows, blankets, silly stuff. Now we're ready for the evening lecture.

<u>Tuesday</u>: Had to sneak two aspirins in the middle of the night. Made it to exercise. Brenda, sweet lady, held my hand and we walked up the hill outside the complex. Tried last Monday. Pretty beat. Did well today. Every morning they read from *God Spoke to Me.* I think it's a channeled book. Start turning pages and ask someone to stop. I need to tape my glasses together. Cheerleader Dr. Mark calls over speaker—"going to class is good." Today— making Rejuvelac. I stopped drinking it about three days ago when I noticed it smelled like what I was expelling after WG implants. Started taking Nystatin again and this morning was not quite so achey. Could move my hands a bit without pain. Right one wasn't all curled up. New noisy neighbor came by and apologized for noise. Said he'd try to keep it down.

The sun feels good. Temperature just right. (I'm sitting here in red sweats—white sleeveless T-shirt—white and pink socks with ruffles and my new, very comfy tennis shoes). I have $250 cash left. Starting to feel alive, not so zombie-like.

Sheri bought me sesame oil for bath and aloe for my eye. She has leukemia and is fighting hard. I'm lying here on my little stool with heels on the toilet lid. Just passing the time, gently massaging my tummy. Some people can't hold it or do it at all. I'm proud. Some people do all this in the tub. I'm getting stronger. This hurt last week—just getting up and down from the floor, on and off this little stool was a challenge.

There's a group of ladies who are pretty close. I can hear them laughing. Two share a room three doors away. I'm kind of on the fringe—but I like being alone and talking with lots of different people. Sheri is still my special friend. Just like camp.

Wednesday: It's official. I'm going to be a three-weeker! Walked up the big hill. Gathered in our circle and Mark announced his mother had died in Israel this morning. They will bury her there. She was 82. It was very touching the way he carried on with the message, breaking down, laughing—telling how she wanted everyone to be happy. He asked his mother to be the one to choose the passage today and it was, "Learn to be at peace." Very appropriate. Most everyone was crying. It is pretty amazing to be here at this time. But life goes on—wheatgrass planting class at 9:30 A.M.

Releasing ceremony on front lawn. An opportunity to send a message to Rachael Solomon, our founder. Rachael—I'll be forever grateful! Thank you. Godspeed in your exciting journey. Release me on my new journey. I want to become more daring—fearless.

Alice, Joyce, the other Paula, Sheri, Diana, and I formed a circle and vowed to keep in touch. A great group of ladies, although we are looking really scruffy.

Happiness is clean laundry.

Friday: We had a nice send-off for Joyce with hugs and tossed wheatgrass in showers like confetti.

Called Randy to tell him how well I was feeling. Headache going away. Just know my body is coming back. Went to class in natural skin care. Ended with cucumbers on eyes. Beets for rouge and lips. Took long nap. Feel pretty stiff but no headache. Don't think I'll venture out with the gang tonight. Just want to go to bed early. Ate uncooked applesauce sitting outside alone. (Wearing beige linen slacks, blue blouse, brown sandals, green specked [WG] socks and hat). The weather is perfect—not too hot. Can sleep without air conditioner. Wow! Another week almost over.

Took a peek at first-weekers' validation group. I was glad I wasn't with them. Our first-weekers were very special—lots of spiritually-minded folks. Interesting vibes—a convergence of strength and power. One of the massage people said something interesting to me—she was asking me how I liked it, and I told her they were terrific. She said—no, not the staff but the wonderful people you meet that come here. She said Rachael wouldn't spend much on maintenance—wanted volunteers to work for room and board. But now that she's gone, there may be lots of changes. Getting the hot tub fixed should be one, I thought, and caulking the bath tubs. I like my room but some are a little old and moldy.

Rash on chest is gone, wrists less swollen, stronger. I believe thing on arm is disappearing—was like a golf ball under skin half-way between wrist and elbow. Now I'm getting what seem to be bedsores or pressure sores on both elbows because I have to use my elbows to push off the floor. Gum line area where tooth was pulled achey today. What's that about?

Talked to sweet Brenda, the Casino dealer, about root canals. She's had swollen glands on side of neck for years. Was wondering if teeth could be the cause. Told my tooth story 'cause they were talking about amalgam fillings. One lady had them taken out all at once—got deathly ill. Too much toxic release for her body to handle. We know about toxicity.

The circle is diminishing. Diana and Alice are leaving. Plucked hairs on chin. Must be feeling livelier. Putting pure aloe on eye. Thinking of WG as a blood transfusion. Going to drink it twice a day from now on. Think I will stay in this room. Decisions, decisions. But it opens to outside for fresh air and I can sit in the sun if I want.

Sneezing, blowing nose—coughing up slimy, thick stuff. WG is pulling it out. Drinking lots of water. Testimonials at lunch were good—mostly by people who've been here before. A man without health insurance (he says the Institute is his medical plan) comes every year with his family to stay well and maintain health. Now to—"Advanced Food Preparation."

Ate dinner with Sheri, Ernie, and Tom. Tom is an attorney and a natural standup. A funny guy. He crocheted some green slippers for our friend Ernie of Ernie Martin's Acting School. I look thin—even to me. People say my eye looks greatly improved. Hope so. Put a poultice on today (as always) and it really stung. Still something bad going on there. Thank goodness the headaches, cheek ache, tooth, or gum ache is gone for the moment. Still have sore back, chest, and throat. I can make my bed so much easier. This week, I'm paying a lady $10 to clean my room. Tom, Sheri, and others were going to Tiajuana. I am feeling stronger but decided to stay here and direct my energies to healing.

Rocky cleaned my room. Smells fresh—she apologized because she couldn't get mold out of tub. It's not too bad. Sheri couldn't stand the mold, went out and bought a caulking gun, scraped her tub with razor blades, and recaulked it. I told her Debbie Reynolds had that room. She could call Debbie and complain.

Looking forward to a week of no classes. I had perfect attendance at classes for two weeks!

This evening five of us pulled lounge chairs into the big room and watched a bad movie. Tom and Ernie went out into the outside world. I may go to town with everyone tomorrow. Will be my last chance to see San Diego. Weighed again. Now only 130 lb. with layers of clothing. Hard to believe—but a much better weight. Felt light. Now—to get in shape. I don't like being a weakling. When I get home I'm going to join the "Y" and lift weights. This was a restful day. I like my new friends.

The WG is pulling tissue stuff out of bowels and now that I'm drinking more—coughing junk up. Rumors are that sixty new people are checking in. Sheri calls us "The Wheatgrass Cult."

It's difficult to eat so many sprouts. They give us such huge portions and everyone feels bad throwing stuff out. Buffet style would be better. I don't know if my stomach is shrinking or if it's just the blandness of the raw food. A baked potato would sure taste good.

Such achey joints! Hopefully, will get better this week.

We went to the mall. Sheri is the prize shopper. I bought a rose quartz crystal to increase confidence, heighten personal expression. It's good for the heart, which Renee said I needed. She said I had a tightness in the heart area. We drove down around the water. San Diego is quite spectacular. Tom drove and was very patient and a good chaperone. Surprised that my energy lasted so long. Got dizzy a few times. How odd to be out after so long—cars—people—smells—all that stimulation.

Back for dinner of sprouts and seed cheese. Felt nauseous. Heart racing. Took hot bath and cold shower. The world can reach out and get you. Everyone OUTSIDE looked kind of frantic. Glad I live where I do.

What a mob scene at dinner. All the new people. We joined hands and filled the whole multipurpose room. Ernie saw an actor he knows and introduced us. You've seem him in lots of movies and TV shows. One of those busy ones whose name you can't remember. He's the chief on "Lois & Clark." I guess he's here to lose weight.

Monday: Didn't sleep well last night. Neck and chest hurt. Lay in bed until chiropractic appointment. Neck wouldn't move but hips cracked all over. Sat in the sun with the girls and talked about weddings. Got some WG to drink and for my eye. Feel like something is being pulled from my body. Really tired and achey.

We went to Ernie's room to watch his wife on "Evening Shade." Ernie wouldn't say anything about the Burt and Loni affair except that he hoped it wouldn't hurt the show. I'm trying to relax but like all the three-weekers I'm thinking about going home. I need to keep gathering strength and healing this week. I want so much to be well when I get off the plane—but maybe that's asking too much. I've made great progress and have the tools. Just have to stick with the program and build. This has been quite a trip. We all agreed we're glad we arrived with this group of people. There are no accidents.

Tuesday: Man, I don't know how I made it at 7:00 A.M. with my cup of WG. I was rocky, dizzy. My heart pounds so during a colonic. She said my bowel was working better—not swelling up so much in one area and releasing faster. Lots of old hard bits—ancient-looking and still mucous. My body is working hard.

After a shower—feel better. One more colonic to go—plus E's & I's, of course.

Okay, I'm listening to my body. Been nauseous off and on all day. The colonic and massage were very intense. I thought I would scream when she rubbed my feet. Bought Epsom salts, plain rice cakes, and three pears, and apples. This will be my dinner. Pears were wonderful.

<u>Wednesday</u>: No exercises. Sore throat. Watermelon for breakfast. Sheri gave me sea salt to clean my crystals. When I did E's & I's this morning a swarm of things came out in a ball. Is this the last of the worms? It sort of plopped out. Icky Poo! Shaved my legs, washed my hair, put poultice on my eye—did two implants, ate three rice cakes. I'm taking my pulse and heading for lunch. (Have on beige shorts, white tank top, white lace socks, and sandals). Hair is still wet so will wear a hat.

<u>Thursday</u>: Sheri's room is upside down. She's in a packing mode. Ready to race her car. Said this isn't just a three-week thing—I'm not going to forget you guys. Everyone is lounging around—recharging. It's quickly coming to an end. I feel very good about this program. I'm much stronger than when I arrived. I'm glad I stayed three weeks. Was very ill! So happy we had enough sense to take charge—to do something unconventional—even radical. It's all so natural. Makes perfect sense. Sheri gave me a medicine pouch with three stones—tourmaline (restoration), jasper (general strength), smoky quartz (enhancement of energy).

Ernie told me to stop rubbing my eye. Tried to get the scoop on Burt and Loni. He's not talking. Very discreet.

Paula brought me a Wendy's baked potato. Smelled better than it tasted. Felt a bit guilty.

Seven of us went to a vegetarian restaurant in Del Mar. Had navy bean soup and very tasty pizza. We walked around and looked at the ocean. Tomorrow is our last day.

<u>Friday</u>: This day has flown by and it's almost time for dinner. After we ate it was time for the regular Friday night talent show. I had called Randy and asked him to mail me some poems he'd written for me. I hadn't been in front of a group in a long time. So I was nervous. (Wore white poet's blouse with ruffled sleeves and lacy tie at neckline, hair piled up). My glasses were taped together and I held a delicate hankie in my right hand. I *very* grandly introduced my poem which was titled "Snot." It kind of summed up how many of us felt.

<u>Snot</u>
Throbbing tissue swells
excreting toasted sludge

which slides and slips by gravity
into the reddish gorge.
The gag reflex regurgitates
in a shapeless lump
a pithy planetoid of snot.
The nut of a decision
not pleasing to the palate
sits reptile-like upon the tongue.
To swallow or expectorate
a primordial dilemma
faced kings and rubes and vagabonds
and even sweet Aunt Emma
As fever racks one's weary brain,
as handkerchiefs pile up,
to wit to stop the leaking,
consider ties to history
post-nasally a-speaking.

They liked it. Laughed and clapped and Sheri wanted a copy. Then we all accepted our WG certificates—stood together in front and cheered. (We were certainly an enthusiastic group.) Then we all did testimonies. I think I carried on too long, but people said it was an inspiration to them—really touched them. It made me feel better. Time to move on. I'm doing all my duties. The Optimum Health show is almost over.

Did my final E's & I's here. Drank WG twice. Went for a short walk. Took two naps. Tried to pack. Talked to Sarah. So young; only twenty-five. She has had hydrogen peroxide IV's and says she is going to beat candida. So many of her friends have chronic fatigue syndrome. The sign of the '90s? Saying good-byes. Some people all packed and ready to leave early.

Saturday: Good-byes at breakfast, hugs, last photos. Gave scarf to Ernie and Tom, Sheri a gold lizard. Paula loved her frilly socks. I'm wearing my WG green dress and vest. Everything is packed, somehow. Still need to close the duffel bag. A large orange cat sneaked into my room and hid under the bed. He's sitting beside me now saying good-byes. Cats are not allowed in the rooms because of people with allergies. They have fleas. But he's very nice. All my dear friends are gone. I have a feeling I'll be seeing them again.

Good-bye, little safe room. It's been great. May the force of wheatgrass be with you. Ashland, here I come.

Chapter 8
Toward More Natural Healing

Linda was the last one off the plane. I was shocked by her appearance. When I hugged her, she felt like a completely different woman than the one I had taken to the airport three weeks before. She didn't look sick exactly. Just small, as if she had shrunk. But she was smiling happily, looking stylish in her green dress, little sandals, and straw hat. She had so many rocks and crystals hanging around her neck I was surprised she could walk. Noble and I were there to greet her and she, of course, started weeping.

"Your eye looks good," said Noble.

"Does it?" she wondered. "I put wheatgrass poultices on my eye every day."

"You lost a lot of weight," I said.

"That's why some people go there—to lose weight. Tom did the best. He lost 35 pounds. He also crocheted seven pairs of slippers and did five skeins on a bedspread."

Noble and I looked at each other, wondering if we really wanted to know what a skein was.

"Who's Tom?"

"Well, three weeks ago he was a fat attorney. But now he's a skinny attorney," she said.

"Is this place a weight reduction clinic?" I asked her as we carried the bags to our car.

"A lot of people go there to lose weight—like Ernie—he's an acting teacher, and Lane, his friend, who is on TV. And Tom, of course. But most of the people there are really sick with cancer, leukemia, MS, chronic fatigue—all kinds of stuff."

"Do they get better?" asked Noble.

"I did," she said in a very small voice.

I had a surprise waiting when we got home. Trays of lush wheatgrass were sprouting all over the house along with sunflower and flax sprouts and jars of alfalfa, red clover, and fenugreek. I had purchased a grinder and was ready to produce the dark green juice for drinking and for the enemas and implants recommended by the Optimum Health Institute people. Linda's two cats were fighting over her lap.

"I'm ready to grind some grass," I told her, pleased that my plan had been executed.

"Let's wait until tomorrow," said Linda without enthusiasm.

During the three weeks that Linda had been in San Diego I had been on vacation from care giving. I had enjoyed the break. A chronically ill person is like a small child in need of constant care and attention. Linda's hands, which had been suddenly twisted and swollen by arthritis had made her even more dependent. With her return, it was back to trying to make sure she got food and water, that her clothes were clean, preparing baths, encouraging exercise, and massaging aching joints and muscles. The optimism and good spirits which had come through the phone lines on my frequent calls to San Diego dissipated quickly on her return to Ashland. It was not that OHI had been unhealthy and unhelpful. We both believed it had been a worthwhile experience. But her high expectations for a "cure" in three weeks had not been realized. In reality she still felt quite poorly. She was puny and weak after three weeks of sticking to a rigorous program of diet and cleansing. In those three weeks she had lost her appetite. Food, which her emaciated body obviously needed, was disgusting to her. She complained about the odors of the meals I cooked. And, as I found out on her second day back when I presented her with two fresh ounces of the dark green juice, she hated wheatgrass! Couldn't bear the smell of it. Refused to drink it. She accepted my offering for use only as an implant. Linda believed she needed to continue her internal cleansing, fearful that worms still lived in the dark, moist recesses of her bowel, certain that the grass was seeking them out, pulling them loose and expelling them in a green deluge.

I enjoyed my routine with the wheatgrass. I loved to be up early on these warm September mornings to watch the light explode orange over Grizzly Peak and bathe our backyard in a fuzzy glow. I would read and try to sit quietly for a period of time and then around eight would choose a tray of wheatgrass and carry it outside to the picnic table.

I assembled my grinder and greased the moving parts with Crisco. I would cut a handful of the clean, green, eight-inch tall grass with a Ginzu knife and feed it into the hopper of the grinder. The first drops of juice would splatter into a cup like jots of dark green blood. As I turned the crank and fed more grass, the small cup would begin to fill, and ground grass would extrude from the grinder. I would pull a hunk of this and chew it like gum. Wheatgrass tasted good to me. It was a pure, sweet, clean taste and refreshed my mouth. The first ounce of juice I drank myself as a reward for this morning duty. An ounce of wheatgrass is a potent drink. It gives one a jolt and a rush of blood to the eyes.

Then I would wake Linda and help her get organized for her E's & I's. She made me leave her wheatgrass juice just outside the bathroom door, complaining all the while that she could smell it anyway and that it was disgusting. While she performed her morning absolutions, I cleaned my equipment and put it away, soaked more seeds, and tended to my planting and watering. I would then harvest some sprouts and put them in plastic bags to be ready for lunch. Linda refused the sprouts too, so they were all mine.

I feared that she was starving. Her breasts and butt had collapsed and skin seemed to sag around her knees. She couldn't open her hands and her elbows were clearly infected with pressure sores. She had a gagging cough and was frequently short of breath. Her eye was still swollen, though not so severely. Most disturbing, after all this, we still did not know what was causing her ever-growing list of symptoms.

While Linda was at Wheat Grass University, our friends Jim and Joyce convinced me to sign up for a Qigong (Chee-gung) class. They were avid practitioners of Tai Chi, and I had been trying to get their advice on which of the many Tai Chi teachers in Ashland to study with. I had never heard of Qigong before. They explained that it was like Tai Chi but more involved with motives of maintaining the body in good health.

Our class met in Lithia Park between the tennis courts and the upper duck pond on a moist lawn which was bordered by tall maple and cedar trees. The lone mulberry tree near the duck pond was bearing fruit, and ducks worked through the grass beneath the large tree eating the berries which were dropping from the heavy branches. Tourists strolled the path on the edge of our training ground waiting for another Shakespeare play to start. There was a steady thunk of tennis balls rebounding from racquets, and the squeak of shoes sliding on the composition court surface.

Our instructor, Fred Epping, who earned his living playing country western guitar, greeted us with a quiet smile. He wore no special costume, just jeans, sweatshirt, and running shoes and said little until it was time to start the class. He gave us a short briefing on Qigong. He told us there were many types of exercise in China called Qigong and that it was a very old practice—perhaps two thousand years old, predating even acupuncture. The form we would learn was called "Wild Goose," named, I decided later, because of the many arm flapping movements involved. Wild Goose Qigong, Fred told us, had been kept a secret by its practitioners until this century. His teacher had learned it from a little Chinese lady who had practiced it in secret—even her husband did not know for nearly her entire life. Fred had studied Qigong, as well as Tai Chi, for more than twenty years and had only recently returned to the United States from Russia, where he had taught Tai Chi and Qigong at the University of Moscow.

There were five parts to Wild Goose Qigong. The first four were designed to maintain or regain health. The fifth was a martial art. We would learn Part One, the intent of which was to move energy (ch'i) through our bodies. The universe, Fred explained quietly as we stood under the tall trees, was made up of energy. This energy was available to us, and we would use Qigong to bring good energy into our bodies, move it through our system's meridians, or energy channels, and then release bad energy from our bodies into the atmosphere. Qigong would be like giving ourselves an acupuncture treatment, and if we practiced with regularity and with the proper visualization it would increase our energy, improve our metabolism, and provide better sleep. In short, it would make us healthier. In time, perhaps even a very short time, we would begin to be able to feel the ch'i moving through our limbs and feel the energy.

In China, many hospitals use Qigong as an integral part of their healing and rehabilitation programs. Many Qigong exercises involve breathing routines which can be done at rest, sitting, standing, or even lying down. Chinese physicians claim many successes using Qigong as a tool to combat chronic diseases, including cancer.

Fred demonstrated the first part of Wild Goose as we sat on the grass near the grazing ducks. It was a baffling array of arm waving, bending, twisting, and handshaking which Fred managed to make look graceful, goose-like, and athletic. I was certain that I could never learn the choreography of this strange dance. Tourists halted to watch Fred bend and swoop and flap his wings. They moved on, remembering they were in Ashland, a place where one might see anything.

Then, he put us in a line—seven rather confused middle-aged and older adults wearing various summer outfits—and taught us the cleansing movement which would begin our exercise, and which is the only movement that can be even vaguely described in writing. Only Jim and Joyce, veterans of many Tai Chi seminars, seemed ready and alert.

Fred asked us to visualize a universe full of energy, to put our left toe forward, left heel off the ground, butt tucked slightly underneath our hips, weight back on our right foot and to turn slightly to the left, reaching out and up with our arms to gather a ball of energy with our hands. Then, taking a quick sharp breath, we were to pull the energy ball down through the top of our heads, our hands now facing our body, elbows out, relaxed, pulling the ball of energy through our face, our neck, and down the left side of our torso; using the energy to cleanse our cells of toxins and poisons; expelling our breath in a slow, continuous stream of air as we pulled the energy ball down our hips, leg, knee, calf, ankle, and finally out our toes and into the ground. We then took a slow step forward, now pointing our right toe on the ground and repeated the entire movement. There were thirty-six steps in the cleansing movement, eighteen left and eighteen right and when we finished, we were standing next to the mulberry tree. The ducks ran and hid in the bushes. I thought I could feel some ch'i.

Linda had not gotten out of bed since her return from Wheatgrass University except to complete her morning exercises with the fresh juice I was squeezing. Her vitality was low. She was weak. Too many times in the past we had tried to wait it out, whatever "it" was. We decided that we should continue to take action, if only for action's sake. Dr. Osterhaus had done a good job of getting her ready to travel. We decided to return to his office to see what other tricks he had up his sleeve. I had been reading up on naturopathy since our first visit to Dr. Osterhaus.

While Linda had been gone, my mother had sent me a novel called *The Road to Wellville*, set at the turn of the century at the health spa in Battle Creek run by the famous Dr. John Harvey Kellogg. The author of the novel, T. Coraghessen Boyle, presented a humorous and rather uncomplimentary painting of life in the Battle Creek Sanitarium, where the inmates received enemas and hydrotherapy, ate strange vegetarian food, and listened to Dr. Kellogg rail against meat and other poisons to the body—a scenario not unlike the one Linda was experiencing in San Diego while I was reading the book. I also read about Jethro Kloss, trained by Dr. Kellogg, who operated a branch of the Battle Creek Sanitarium and sold the health foods developed by Dr. Kellogg and his brother. Though not a trained physician, Jethro Kloss learned and used natural methods of healing in reaction to the dangerous drugs commonly used by medical doctors in attempting to heal the sick. In the mid-nineteenth century the primary tools of allopathic medicine were mercury pills and bloodletting. These techniques had devastating side effects, and many people viewed allopathic medicine as dangerous. Practitioners of herbal or Indian medicine gained a great following. Lay practitioners and educated physicians who used steam baths and herbs became known as "eclectics," and this practice evolved over time into naturopathy. As with Jethro Kloss, who was a logical descendent of the Indian school doctors, emphasis was on natural living, food, and herbs. In the compendium of the Kloss family called *Back to Eden,* Jethro Kloss also describes his ideas on cooking, hydrotherapy, massage, and enemas—all important to natural healing. In the early days of the botanicals, those healers who prescribed herbs, Lobelia inflata was the primary herb. Jethro Kloss described it as "one of the first remedies a kind Providence has blessed mankind with." He described lobelia as being excellent for a cough: ". . .relief will be experienced in minutes. . .But how is this result brought about? The properties of the lobelia, by immediate action on the muscular and mucous parts of the esophagus, glottis, larynx, windpipe, and bronchial tubes, cause immediate relaxation; the parts previously contracted are made to expand and breathing is made easier." Linda was having attacks where she felt her throat was closing up on her and that she could not breathe. I bought tincture of lobelia and administered it when she had these attacks. It always brought relief. The herbalists had caught my attention.

On our next visit to Dr. Osterhaus I asked him for a book about naturopathy to read while Linda had hydrotherapy. I learned that naturopathy could only be licensed in a few states—seven to be exact: Alaska, Washington, Montana, Oregon, Hawaii, Arizona, and Connecticut. Clearly, not many people were able to avail themselves of natural treatment, being forced by supply and demand economics to seek help from allopathic medicine, which as far as they knew, was the only medicine. This explained the California license plates we had seen in Dr. Osterhaus' driveway on our first visit.

Naturopaths believe the body has great power to heal itself and that physicians are only catalysts in the process, using natural nontoxic methods and exercising their responsibility as teachers to educate and guide their patients into a healthy life style and mental attitude. Additionally, they believed that the cause of disease rather than its symptoms should be the focus of treatment. Symptoms, Dr. Osterhaus told us, are the body's expressions of the healing process. They should not be suppressed.

The tools of the profession were acupuncture, homeopathy, nutrition, herbal medicine, hydrotherapy, massage, manipulation, and counseling. Many naturopaths, including Dr. Osterhaus, were competent in minor surgery techniques. Our local health food store owner had told me how Dr. Osterhaus had sewed up his son after a serious skating accident and described the wounds as healing quickly and perfectly. I later learned that certain naturopaths could use noninvasive techniques to cure hernias and hemorrhoids. Some naturopaths could deliver babies. A lot could happen in the family room of Dr. Osterhaus' suburban home.

I had been charting Linda's complaints and keeping track of them on my computer to present to Dr. Osterhaus. In that period of time following her stay at OHI she had the following symptoms: nausea, bloating, flatulence, heartburn, itchy ears, ringing in ears, mood swings, anxiety, irritability, depression, fatigue, apathy, watery eyes, swollen and sticky eyelids, blurred vision, headaches, dizziness, irregular heartbeat, rapid or pounding heartbeat, chest pain, painful joints, arthritis, stiffness, muscle aches, weakness, chest congestion, asthma, shortness of breath, difficulty breathing, poor concentration, poor physical coordination, chronic coughing, gagging with frequent need to clear her throat, sore throat, discolored tongue, canker sores, stuffy nose, scabs inside the nose, hair loss, weight loss, and frequent urination.

I was using as my checklist the Metabolic Clearing Therapy Testing Scale, published by HealthComm Inc., a company in Gig

Harbor, Washington, dedicated to research, education, and nutritional management in the field of health maintenance and preventive medicine. Dr. Bart had gone to one of their seminars and sent me the workbook, *Advances in the Diagnosis and Treatment of the Chronically Ill Patient*. It was becoming apparent to me that I was dealing with someone who was, in fact, chronically ill. The fact that she had so many symptoms from the chronic fatigue checklist, including the swollen eye, led me to believe that this could be chronic fatigue. But what caused it? I no longer felt it was a spider bite. The experts seemed confused over a definition.

In the workbook was an article from the *Annals of Internal Medicine* titled "Chronic Fatigue Syndrome: A Working Case Definition." The sixteen M.D.'s who authored the article wrote: "The chronic fatigue syndrome is currently an operational concept designed for research purposes that physicians must recognize not necessarily as a single disease but as a syndrome—a complex of potentially related symptoms that tend to occur together—that may have several causes." Clearly, they didn't know what it was either. The thrust of this article was that these doctors wanted to change the name of something called the "Epstein Barr virus syndrome" to "chronic fatigue syndrome" because they felt that Epstein Barr virus (EBV) was not the sole causative factor in chronic fatigue. Epstein Barr was also known as "chronic mononucleosis." Linda had mono when she was in high school.

The Centers for Disease Control had a definition for chronic fatigue syndrome (CFS):

1. Fatigue has lasted six months.
2. A physician has ruled out any mimicking diseases.
3. For at least six months, at least eight of the following had persisted or reoccurred:
     a. chills, fever, or rash
     b. sore throat
     c. swollen lymph glands
     d. unexplained general muscle weakness
     e. fatigue for twenty-four hours after exercise
     f. headaches unlike any previously experienced
     g. joint pain without swelling or redness
     h. forgetfulness
     i. irritability

j. confusion
k. inability to concentrate
l. depression
m. disturbed sleep

We had numbers 1 and 3 without a doubt. But how could we know diseases which mimicked CFS had been ruled out? The only diagnosis we had received was Candida albicans. Our sixteen- doctor article warned: "Other clinical conditions that may produce similar symptoms must be excluded through evaluation based on history, physical examination, and appropriate laboratory findings. These conditions include malignancies; auto immune disease; localized infection (such as occult abscess); chronic or sub acute bacterial disease (such as endocarditis, Lyme disease, or tuberculosis, fungal disease and parasitic disease, disease related to human immuno-deficiency virus (HIV) infection, chronic psychiatric disease. . ., chronic inflammatory disease (such as. . ..chronic hepatitis), neuromuscular disease (such as multiple sclerosis. . .), endocrine disease (such as hypothyroidism. . .or diabetes mellitus). . ..side effects of chronic medication or other toxic agent (such as a chemical solvent, pesticide, or heavy metal); or other known or defined chronic pulmonary, cardiac, gastrointestinal, hepatic, venal, or hematologic disease."

This was about the most maddening thing I had ever read. What they were saying to me was what I already knew. You need a diagnosis. And if you don't have any other disease known to western man and you're still sick, then you've got chronic fatigue syndrome.

My guess was that somewhere in that long listing of "other clinical conditions" was the answer(s) to our question. We had visited many doctors seeking a diagnosis. Several things had been ruled out, but no definitive diagnosis had materialized. So who was going to rule out the "other clinical conditions," and how were they going to do it? The medical system was organized, through their insistence on specialization, to look at one set of organs or systems at a time. For the patient it was like throwing darts. You had to be lucky enough to walk into the right office.

The office we were in now was Dr. Osterhaus's. He studied the lists of symptoms very carefully. "This is really good," he said. "I wish everyone would give me this much detail." Dr. Osterhaus suggested that Dr. Peter's diagnosis of candida had been correct and that Linda should go back on Nystatin which was a natural substance he could prescribe. It was also important to eliminate sugar from the diet. He carefully filled out a medication schedule for Nystatin, caprilic acid (which also attacked candida), acidophilus to build up good bacteria, garlic (another anti-fungal), multivitamins to boost vitality, digestive enzymes to assist absorption of nutrients, bromelin and PABA with tyrosine (anti-inflammatories), B-12, and folate.

"Continue with the baths," he told her. "Do you still have elderberry and yarrow? That's a good one. Add some sea salt and apple cider vinegar."

"Have you ever had the test for Epstein Barr?" he asked.

"I don't think so," I told him.

"It's expensive; about $200, I think," said Dr. Osterhaus.

"I'm sure we haven't had that one. But let's get it," I said.

"If you have Epstein Barr," he told Linda as he finished a B-12 shot and began a hydrotherapy treatment, "we may have to send you to Dr. Turska for ozone therapy. I don't have an ozone machine, so I can't do it here. I just sent an Epstein Barr patient to him. She called me and says she's much better already. Dr. Turska is an old-time healer. One of my teachers. He's a wizard."

"Where is he?" I asked, hoping for Medford or Eugene.

"He's in Mist," said Dr. Osterhaus.

I'd never heard of Mist but would soon know it quite well.

When we left the office Dr. Osterhaus gave us two lab prescriptions one—for EBV; the other for HIV. "You might as well get checked for HIV so we can rule that out." As we drove to the lab Linda tore up the piece of paper requesting the HIV test. "I'm not having HIV," she said, looking straight ahead.

Through the rest of September we went for hydrotherapy and B-12 shots nearly every day. They seemed to provide a psychological, if not a physical, lift. Dr. Osterhaus was concerned about Linda's lack of vitality and anxiously awaited the blood test which would tell if his diagnosis of Epstein Barr virus was correct. During several of our visits he told us stories about Dr. Turska, his mentor, eighty-five years old and still practicing, offering therapies such as ozone and hernia repair which his own state naturopathic association was enjoining him to cease. According to Dr. Osterhaus, Dr.

Turska had been doing ozone therapy for forty or more years with exceptional results. He invented and built his own ozone generators which he sold to other practitioners and which were available to patients for home use. I had read a pamphlet on candidiasis by a Dr. Donsbach, who ran a clinic in Mexico using hydrogen peroxide injections to cure a variety of diseases. "Donsbach does it differently," Dr. Osterhaus told me. "He uses H_2O_2, hydrogen peroxide. Dr. Turska uses pure ozone. The therapeutic result is probably the same. But at the Donsbach Clinic they remove some blood, infuse it with H_2O_2 and then transfuse it back into your systems. Dr. Turska injects ozone into the portal vein."

"Where's that?" I asked.

"In the rectum," was his answer.

As it turned out, the blood test did show antibodies which pointed to Epstein Barr virus as the culprit. I was disappointed that Dr. Osterhaus would not be able to effect a cure in his family room for us. It was a comfortable place, nonthreatening, unintimidating, only five minutes from our home and, compared with most doctor's offices, inexpensive. But based on Dr. Osterhaus' recommendation, and knowing little about what ozone therapy was, we decided to go to Mist, assuming that ozone therapy was a possible knockout punch and actually encouraged that it might be slightly illegal. Based on the little I knew, using oxygen in the various forms to heal made some sense. It was a key element on the planet, critical to maintenance of life. With all the pollution of our air (O_2) and pollution of our water (H_2O), it seemed logical that ozone (O_3) or hydrogen peroxide (H_2O_2) could have health benefits. Everyone knew that household hydrogen peroxide was an antiseptic which was effective and inexpensive. I had used it on wounds and even as a mouthwash. Why wouldn't it kill bacteria, viruses, or parasites in our systems?

I called Bart to ask what he knew about ozone therapy. He knew that this therapy was widespread in Germany, where more than three thousand physicians were using it to treat a variety of diseases. He told me that hundreds, even thousands of AIDs patients who could afford it were traveling to Germany for ozone therapy with apparently good results. "The FDA hasn't approved ozone therapy in the U.S., so anyone who does it probably keeps it quiet," he told me.

It wasn't too hard to figure out why the FDA, which I had been told was staffed with M.D.'s and lots of former pharmaceutical executives, wouldn't want to approve something as simple as ozone therapy. Ozone, like vitamins, herbs, and other supplements would be difficult, if not impossible to protect under patent laws. Ozone, which apparently could be self-administered at home, would be a significant threat to hospitals and pharmaceutical companies if it were at all effective. If ozone were as effective against cancer, for instance, as its proponents claimed, it could put a serious dent into the cancer treatment business which relies on a process of surgery and chemotherapy/radiation which costs thousands of dollars. It was another example in the history of U.S. medicine in which a natural therapy like ozone was suppressed in favor of unnatural therapies like drugs or chemicals (which poison the body with toxic side effects), surgery (which too often is just butchery), and radiation (which burns the tissues). How far had we really come from the days of mercury pills and bloodletting?

A week later, Dr. Osterhaus reported that the blood tests indicated Epstein Barr. He recommended ozone therapy and we made plans to travel once again.

Chapter 9
The Wizard of Ozone

We got the blood test results on a Friday and I called Dr. Turska's office that afternoon. A woman who answered the phone said we could come in on the following Monday at 1:00 P.M. Linda was pleased we could get in so soon. She was anxious for her cure. I asked her how many treatments were usually needed. The woman said, "About ten." It seemed we would be gone for two weeks. That's all we knew. It was with a great deal of faith and/or an equal amount of stupidity that I loaded the car and set out for Mist, Oregon, which was located west of Portland—a seven-hour drive from our home. I was trying to bring some logic to bear on the problem but, in reality, we were quite desperate and had reached the point of being willing to try just about anything that seemed reasonable. We got into the car with a great desire to believe that ozone was the panacea we were seeking.

Linda was very weak and uncomfortable. She also had a tendency to car sickness which was exacerbated by the fact that she was nauseous most of the time to start with. On leaving Dr. Osterhaus' office she asked him if he had anything for car sickness. He left for a few minutes and returned with a small glass tube filled with white pellets and labeled "Ipec."

"This is a homeopathic remedy," he told her. Put three or four pellets under your tongue if you're feeling nauseous. It will relieve nausea. It is a minute dose of ipecac—the substance you would take to make you vomit. The homeopathic remedy is quite diluted and has the opposite result."

I promised Linda we wouldn't drive all the way the first day. She slept late and we then loaded the car for the trip to Mist and left in the early afternoon. We were off to see the Wizard. The Wizard of Ozone. "The Wizard of O," sang Linda in a feeble, raspy voice. We drove to McMinnville, where I had graduated from Linfield College, and checked into the Safari Motel. In the morning, while

Linda rested, I drove across town to the campus to look around. Linfield looks like a college; red brick buildings set off by a grove of old oaks, tree-lined walks, and a large athletic complex. In the thirty-some years since I had graduated, the college, once known primarily for its championship football teams, had grown in stature academically. The physical plant had changed too, with several new buildings constructed in the Linfield style. During my time at Linfield there had been freshman beanies and mandatory chapel for underclassmen. The Baptists had founded and supported the institution for most of its history, but my impression from reading alumni newsletters was that the religious affiliation had weakened in recent years.

I walked through the oaks past the president's house and down a hill to Cozine Creek, realizing I had never walked down there before. This was a very small campus, and standing on the bridge over the creek, I had the revelation that when I was a student there, I had lived in an extremely small world. I had not been adventurous or very curious and had left the comfort of the dormitory, classroom, or library only when led away by a friend or roommate. I had studied hard and had regurgitated my lessons into little blue exam booklets to earn "A's" and the approval of my professors. In the swale by the creek, I could now see plants I recognized from recent walks led by my friend, Thoreau. Where had Thoreau been during my Linfield years? Why hadn't my educational experience stimulated an ability to challenge rather than repeat?

I walked back up the hill and on to a concrete path between buildings. Dozens of students walked briskly past me seeking an education, whatever that might mean. I wanted to stop a couple of them to remind them to read Thoreau. That was the only advice I could conjure up. I returned to my car realizing that my education hadn't begun at Linfield. No doubt that was my fault. All I had learned was what they put on my plate. I had done what was expected of a bright high school graduate—gone off to college and graduated in four years. In retrospect, I had little to show for it except a degree which qualified me for certain job interviews. But driving away from Linfield, I knew that my education had begun much later. Or, perhaps it was just beginning.

We drove through the coastal mountains west of Portland, winding through woods and along streams, climbing gradually and passing through small towns which had been wounded by excess logging. In many parts of the northwest where cutting trees had been the primary source of income, nature had been altered by the relentless harvesting of the big trees. Ecosystems were out of balance, creating a kind of chronic illness which affected the land and streams and the people who lived there. It was another illness for which there was no apparent cure.

Mist, when we finally found it, was located in a small valley surrounded by clear-cut hills. It had once been a prosperous logging village with mills and many residents engaged in cutting the logs or servicing those who did. Now, Mist was more or less an intersection of two roads. There was a school, a general store, and Dr. Turska's Bio-Medical Clinic. The clinic wasn't fancy. It consisted of two old mobile homes set at right angles to each other, separated from the doctor's even older house and sheds by a gravel driveway. It was shabby looking, but the parking area in front was full of cars with license plates from Arizona, California, Washington, and Oregon. Mist was not easy to get to but others were apparently making the trip.

Linda was exhausted and overwrought, suffering from high expectations. I helped her out of the car and into the waiting room which was a pop-out addition stuck onto the middle portion of the modular office. There were two waiting areas separated by a sliding door. Beyond the slider was a counter and a little lady with wispy white hair. I sat Linda down in one of the two old beat-up reclining rocking chairs which furnished the outer waiting room. The elderly lady behind the counter was very sweet, but she had never heard of us. We were not in the appointment book.

"I talked to a woman on Friday," I said. "We drove all the way from Ashland. Dr. Osterhaus sent us."

She studied the appointment book and looked over her shoulder. "People just keep coming," she said. "I'd like to retire, but they just keep coming. So many people are sick."

She gave me a long form to fill out and I returned to the outer waiting room with a clipboard and a pencil.

"Is there a problem?" asked Linda.

"No," I said. "No problem."

I completed the form and laid it on the counter but the elderly woman had disappeared. There were no other people in the waiting area to go with the three or four cars in the parking lot. I studied the small space. On one wall was a plaque which said, "Psychiatrist—one floor up," and a framed certificate making the doctor a fellow in the Nutrition Society. On a bulletin board was a yellowed news article about Bo Gritz, the former special forces officer who had run for president of the United States. In the article Mr. Gritz stated that, if elected, he would give all HIV-positive patients ozone therapy, which he described as a proven remedy for AIDS.

A very sick man came into the waiting area from inside the clinic. His face was twisted and painfully bent by a raw-looking tumor which began below and then encapsulated his ear. He sat in a straight-back chair and stared down at the ugly orange carpeting. I looked at him and then looked away again. There were dead flies on the slider rail of the glass door. The tumor man was very uncomfortable and was constantly clearing his throat. In his hand he clutched a stack of checkbooks and a copy of *The Pelican Brief*.

I glanced at Linda who was staring at the sick man. Tears streamed down her cheeks. I saw the doctor pass through the space behind the reception counter. He stood there briefly in front of a floor-to-ceiling shelf stacked with bottles and jars. The doctor was very old and very thin. His hair was white and neatly barbered, parted and combed back. He stood very straight and looked kindly and helpful in his white doctor's coat. He disappeared and the receptionist, whom I later deduced was Mrs. Turska, reappeared. I stood and pushed the questionnaire which answered questions about Linda towards her.

"Will we be able to see the doctor?" I asked.

"Oh, yes," she said.

"We were going to take the afternoon off but. . .." At this point a toilet flushed and Dr. Turska emerged, drying his hands very carefully with a white cotton towel. Mrs. Turska handed him Linda's forms.

"Martin sent Linda up to see us," she said to the doctor.

Dr. Turska picked up the questionnaire and scanned it, then indicated I should bring Linda into his office.

In the tiny office there was no room for me to sit. While Dr. Turska read Linda's medical history, I read the walls, which were covered with diplomas, certificates, profuse notes of thanks from former patients, and an 8½-by-11-inch black-and-white autographed photo of a vaguely familiar actor. His desk was strewn with papers, and books were stacked on end. The working portion of his desk was dominated by a new fax machine.

"Well, you've had a time" he said to Linda putting down the questionnaire. "You see, candida and Epstein Barr will mimic lots of diseases. They're just like syphilis was in the old days. They mimic arthritis and pneumonia and the flu. You'll have a symptom here, then one there, and then one will pop up over here," he said tapping her on the knee. "That eye's probably swollen up because your liver is toxed. It's working too hard."

"Will the ozone help?" I asked.

"Oh sure," he said confidently. "The ozone will clean her up. It will kill all the virus and bacteria and parasites."

"Will it really kill HIV?" I wondered.

"Certainly," said the old doctor. "I was treating lots of AIDS people here with good results, but my wife and my young partner thought we should stop because they were afraid our regular patients would quit coming if they knew the AIDS people were here.

"How are your bowels moving?" he suddenly asked Linda.

"I'm taking enemas," she answered.

"No good," said Dr. Turska. "How much fiber are you taking?"

"None," I answered.

"We'll get you some fiber," he said. "Very important to get the bowels working properly. What's the matter with Martin anyway?" he asked, referring to Dr. Osterhaus. "He should get an ozone machine; then you wouldn't have to drive all the way up here."

"I got the feeling he felt he couldn't quite afford one," I said.

"Phooey!" said Dr. Turska. "I told him to come up here and I'd help him build one. Wouldn't cost much. You need to give him a kick in the butt when you get home. If a few more would do this treatment, I could retire. I came up here to retire but people keep coming from all over."

"Well, also, I think he's worried about your state medical society. He said they were trying to get you to stop doing this therapy," I told him.

"That's why I've got this damn fax machine," he said. "I'm waiting to hear from my attorney. Found a mean attorney. He's an Indian—a warrior. I'm so old I can tell them to go to hell. Our association is losing its courage. They want to be socially acceptable. They don't want to upset the medical doctors. They can all go to hell!"

"Linda," he said suddenly with a soft tone of voice. "Let's get you ready and we'll get started knocking out this Epstein Barr."

"Have you ever had a fax machine?" he asked me as Linda left the small office.

"Yes, I have," I replied.

"Well, stay in here and fix that damn thing. I've been waiting all day for an important letter from that attorney."

We had been told that the Turskas were open only on Monday, Wednesday, and Friday, but fortunately for us, this week they would also open Tuesday and Thursday because of the out-of-town-ers they were attempting to accommodate. We scheduled appointments for the remainder of the week and got back in our car, for there were no accommodations for travelers in Mist. We headed for Clatskannie, which was thirty minutes away on a winding downhill road through the tall trees and clear-cuts. In Clatskannie we checked into, then out of, the motel that Mrs. Turska had recommended. It was noisy and uncomfortable. We kept driving, and in fifteen more minutes crossed a high bridge over the Columbia River into Longview, Washington.

I decided that if we were going to be here two weeks we had better be comfortable and ended up in our new home—the Red Lion Inn in Kelso, which hid behind Interstate 5. We lay on a king-size bed and Linda described her first treatment while she sipped the fibrous drink recommended by our new doctor.

"I feel like the ozone is doing something," she said. "I can feel it in my chest. It's warm. It feels like it's chewing through that congestion."

"How did it get in your chest if they put it up your butt?" I asked.

"I breathed it, too," she told me. "First they put me in this tiny room on a small cot and Mrs. Turska covered me up with blankets and I breathed it through a mask. It was very comforting. Mrs. Turska is so sweet. Just like a little grandma."

"Then what?" I asked.

"Then they took me into another room. It was sort of like an operating room. There was a big oxygen tank hooked up to a machine like the one I had been breathing from. She gave me a gown and I put it on. Mrs. Turska helped me with my shoes and got me up on the table. She's small, but she's strong. I was on my side and the doctor came in and washed up and put on his rubber gloves and put the ozone in."

"How'd he do it?" I wanted to know.

"I don't know exactly," she said.

"Didn't you ask questions?"

"No," she said with some irritation. "Why don't you come watch?"

We spent two full weeks at the Red Lion, and Linda had ten intravenous ozone treatments. On each scheduled appointment day we would get into the car and drive across the river and up into the hills along the winding road through the ferny woods and the clear-cuts. Linda used the Ipec to fight car sickness and it worked. The trip took about fifty minutes on the narrow road with delays for road construction. Finally, we would wind down a short hill into the narrow valley, past the cemetery and the white frame grade school, past the store which had been established in the 1895, and into the clinic parking lot. The tumor man was usually there and the mother and daughter from Bellevue, Washington, who had matching cases of chronic fatigue syndrome, the woman who always wore a scarf on her head, and the retarded girl, who sat angrily in the waiting room with her curly head down, staring at the carpet, mumbling in a way that sounded like cursing, expressing for all of us the frustration of the chronically ill. "Dis and dat!" she mumbled, her anger reaching a crescendo. "Dis and dat!"

The pace in the clinic was slow and relaxed. Mrs. Turska would occasionally take a break from her labors and come to the outer waiting room where she would lie down on an old chiropractic table and flip the switch which unloosed a roller, that massaged her back. There was little conversation among the patients, who all seemed weak and tired but universally in agreement that ozone therapy was making them get well. The ladies from Bellevue tried to convince me to sell Sunrider herbal products. The tumor man was always silent, though after his young, blond daughter picked him up, the woman who always wore a scarf on her head would invariably run up to Mrs. Turska to suggest that his tumor was getting smaller. The lady who always wore a scarf on her head was scheduled for surgery. She believed, I deduced from her conversations with Mrs. Turska, that she no longer needed the operation, that the ozone was curing whatever problem she had. Mrs. Turska later told Linda that the scarf lady's adult children had stormed into the clinic one day, demanding to know what Dr. Turska was doing to their mother. They shouted at him, called him a quack, and left. She decided to go through with the surgery to placate her children.

Every third day or so Dr. Turska would ask me to fix his fax machine. I'd owned a fax machine, but had never repaired one before. Luckily, it was just a matter of adjusting the paper. He didn't seem to get it. I asked him about Dr. Donsbach, who had a clinic in Mexico which used oxygen therapy. Dr. Turska told me that Donsbach charged too much. "One lady paid $6,000 for two weeks," he reported with evident disgust.

His disdain for profiteering on illness was evident. The Turskas charged $55 for a single session of ozone therapy. So our first two weeks with room, food, gas, and some odds and ends would cost about $2,000. Most of that was for living expenses. Much cheaper than going to Mexico.

"How many treatments will she need?" I kept asking him.

"Maybe eight," he said one day.

"Maybe twelve," he said another.

Most afternoons, after the treatment, Linda felt well enough to walk. There was a slough next to the hotel and a dike with a walking path on top, and she could walk a mile or so in comfort. Dr. Turska had sold me a book on oxygen therapies written, he said, by one of his patients. The book recommended hydrogen peroxide baths, and each evening I'd pour four pints of H_2O_2 into a hot bath and let Linda soak. I had to help her in and out of the bath because of her weak hands and sore elbows. Her rear end was so skinny we put a folded towel in the tub for her to sit on. The baths were soothing but the ozone was creating another die-off reaction. Linda slept poorly. She ached and would wake me in the middle of the night to massage her so she could go back to sleep.

Dr. Turska had convinced me to buy a small ozone generator which would clean the air in our house.

"Take it in your motel room. It will get rid of dust and molds, mites, and cat dander. Ozone is O_3," he continued. "Three oxygen molecules. Ozone isn't very stable. That third molecule will attach itself to a particle of dust and it'll drop right out of the air. What you have left is O_2, fresh oxygen to replenish the breathable air. We were just in San Francisco to the meeting of the International Ozone Society. Lots of Germans there. They're way ahead of us."

"They use it in other countries?" I asked.

"Very common," said the doctor, "especially in Germany and Russia. There's all manner of uses for oxygen," he continued. "Industry is the biggest user. Lots of cities purify their water with ozone. Reduces the need for chemicals."

"The fax machine is working again," I told him. I was glad he kept asking me to fix it. I was feeling a part of the staff. I now had the run of the place and was aware that the state Naturopathic Association had requested that he cease and desist the building and selling of medical ozone generators.

"How are you doing with the association?" I asked.

"We're going down there this weekend for a meeting. They can all go to hell. I used to be president of the national association before most of these fellows were even practicing. Ozone helps people, dammit!" he shouted, slapping the fax machine as it started beeping. "Fix that thing, will ya!" he ordered, as he went looking for patients.

Linda was feeling better the second week, and this was very encouraging. Dr. Turska felt she was improving. Mrs. Turska thought so too. We felt good about our trip to Mist. The ozone seemed to be doing its job, and we decided to return home after the tenth intravenous treatment. I finally asked if I could watch.

I followed Linda into the exam room. The place had an ancient quality to it. In the bathroom were old medical appliances. On one wall of the bathroom was a board with antique-looking glass tubes stuck onto wooden pegs. The tubes, not used for years, were covered with a light coating of cobwebs. In the exam room was the ozone generator and a large oxygen tank with tubes and hoses running back and forth. The generator had several gauges. On the wall was a single, framed black-and-white photograph. A patient lay on a table like the one in the exam room. The table was in an operating theater and was surrounded by about twenty doctors wearing suits. A young doctor Turska stood poised beside the patient's bare abdomen holding a large hypodermic, frozen in time, the attentive doctors waiting for him to finish the procedure.

"I'm fixing a hernia in that picture," said Dr. Turska coming into the room. "Inject a solution into the tissue around the hernia. Clears it right up. They don't want me to do that either. But it works. So, I keep doing it."

"Now, who do we have here?" he asked his wife. "This is Linda," she said.

"Are you still here?" he asked her. "I thought you were going home."

"This afternoon," said Linda. "I mean as soon as you're done."

Dr. Turska washed up and put on his latex gloves, as did Mrs. Turska. He adjusted dials on the ozone generator and it began to hum. I could get a whiff of the acrid ozone smell which I associated with electricity. Connected to the machine was a flexible tube and to the end of this tube the doctor hooked an appliance which looked like a primitive gun. It had a sort of trigger and a long needle instead of a barrel. He held the needle near his cheek and squeezed the trigger, smelling, I supposed, the ozone.

Another appliance was produced which looked like a plastic garlic press. This was lathered up with lubricating gel and inserted into Linda's rectum. I had pressed myself against the wall next to a small sink to maintain a clear line of sight and winced as the large tube disappeared. Mrs. Turska stood opposite the doctor who sat on an adjustable stool. She reached across Linda who was on her left side, presenting her rear end to me and Dr. Turska. Mrs. Turska was using both hands to pull Linda's cheeks apart. For an eighty-two-year old woman she had quite a grip. Then Dr. Turska pulled and removed the core of the plastic appliance, which seemed to be about one and one-half inches in diameter, leaving a tunnel to the portal vein. He inserted the long needle into the plastic tube, positioned it and squeezed the trigger several times.

"When you administer ozone this way," he told us, "50 percent of the ozone goes directly to the liver. The rest goes into the bloodstream."

The intravenous part of the procedure didn't last very long. He removed the plastic tube and changed the needle for a nonthreatening plastic tip and reinserted it.

"Now I'm infusing ozone into the rectum. This will travel through the large and small intestine and clean them up. Then we'll have Linda breathe some more ozone to get it working on her respiratory tract."

I followed him out of the room. "Is it okay if we leave?" I asked. "Has she had enough treatments?"

"It's hard to say," said Dr. Turska. "More would be better. But it might be better for her to go home and rest. You can always come back. We'll be here if they haven't shut us down."

Later, Linda gave Mrs. Turska a big hug and an azalea plant we'd picked up in Clatskannie that morning. Mrs. Turska was clearly pleased. We paid our final bill, and Dr. Turska gave Linda a herbal remedy called Essiac which was a combination of several familiar plants.

"This can cure cancer," he said. "The lady in Canada who came up with it was put in jail. It's a wonderful remedy."

Linda was feeling better. We said our good-byes. We liked the Turskas, who stood behind the counter, two very old people, dedicated to helping their patients, operating out of a shabby mobile home in the run-down village of Mist, Oregon.

The curly-haired retarded girl sat in the waiting room as we walked out the front door. "Dis an dat," she mumbled at us. "Dis and dat."

Chapter 10
The Thief of Vitality

Linda stayed in bed for an entire week after returning from Mist. This was very disturbing. She had been making progress during her two weeks of intravenous ozone therapy. Back home, the progression seemed to stop. We searched for theories. Perhaps it was her period. Maybe the die-off of pathogens was continuing. Possibly her body needed rest to regenerate. Healing takes time.

We had been at this for a year now, seeking a solution to the problem. However, at this point, we had not even clearly identified the cause of the illness. The many doctors and practitioners we had consulted had suggested a few possibilities: spider bite, allergy, dust mites, tapeworms, malagia, Epstein Barr. Based on what I had read, I believed it was fair to call Linda's illness "chronic fatigue syndrome" since she had all the symptoms. The available literature on CFS was not very satisfying. There were therapies but none were particularly useful. There was a national chronic fatigue syndrome support group that one could join, but which offered no apparent solutions other than the consolation of knowing there were many other sufferers.

It seemed to me that within the cumulative mind of medicine there should be someone with the capability to diagnose the specific cause and remedy for a chronically ill person. I was a subscriber to America Online (AOL), an information network that connected my computer to thousands of other users. I checked the bulletin boards for information on Epstein Barr Virus and chronic fatigue syndrome. There were many messages which reflected the abject frustration of people in a constant state of suffering, people who verged on loss of hope.

I found on AOL a curious article copyrighted by the National Chronic Fatigue Syndrome Association, which I supposed was an organization of certain medical professionals and not to be confused with CFIDS (Chronic Fatigue and Immune Dysfunction Syndrome), the patient advocacy group. Why is it called CFIDS and not CFS for chronic fatigue syndrome? Because the patient advocacy group believes that CFS "trivializes" the illness. In short, CFS is not politically correct. It was pathetic that these unwell people, who had no cure to look forward to, should be reduced to fighting for a description which would not trivialize their condition.

The article in question was called "The Thief of Vitality" and described CFS as an "illness of unknown origin." "CFS," the article continued, "is diagnosed by exclusion of all other illnesses known to modern science." This meant to me that CFS is what you have if you don't have anything else with a name and you can't get out of bed.

They referred to the list of symptoms which I had earlier discovered in the "Annals of Internal Medicine" article. Then they listed a series of questions and answers which, paraphrased, were:

Q. Who diagnoses it?

A. A reputable clinician.

My question: (Where does one get the list of reputable clinicians? And, what makes them reputable?)

Q. Who are the authorities on CFS?

A. Any clinician should be able to diagnose it.

My question: (How can there be *authorities* on a disease for which there is no known cause and no known cure?)

Q. Are there tests used to diagnose?

A. Not yet.

My comment: (That doesn't seem to stop doctors from ordering many expensive tests.)

Q. How long will I be sick?

A. Some medical professionals feel symptoms can peak out in one to three years in some patients, while other patients seem to have consistent symptoms that have several years' duration.

My comment: (No comment.)

Q. Is this related to AIDS?

A. No.

My comment: (Some good news for a change.)

Q. Is it fatal?

A. We have heard of a few suicides.

My comment: (A very flip answer to a serious question.)

Q. What kind of treatment is available?

A. Reputable physicians treat symptoms ONLY, refer patients to credible support groups, and provide educational materials to learn to *cope with CFS* (emphasis mine). One should determine that the physician is interested in the patient's well-being and not his/her bank account. Improper treatments can include intravenous hydrogen peroxide, intravenous vitamin C, Chinese herbs, and blood warming treatments. (I made a note to look into blood warming—the only improper treatment they listed we hadn't had yet.) For those "CFS experts" promising a cure, one finds the treatment is extremely expensive, requires payment in advance, and comes with no guarantee. We know of no refund offers for those who don't get well. Proper nutrition (recommended by the National Dairy Association) and rest can be beneficial.

My question: (How much more propaganda against alternative therapies can be packed into one paragraph? And, do M.D.'s ever give refunds?)

Q. What is the misinformation about CFS?

A. That it can be cured. . .

My question: (Then who needs reputable physicians?)

Q. What can individual patients do?

A. Join a support group. . . . .

My question: (How much does a reputable physician charge for that advice?)

Q. Are there any good books on CFS?

A. There are approximately fifteen books available on CFS which have been reviewed for medical accuracy. . . .

My question: (Why would anyone want to read even one book which offered neither the cause of the disease or the solution?)

Q. Where is the legitimate research being conducted?

The answer to this question went on and on, but I thought the use of the word "legitimate" summed up an article which provided no helpful information, yet went at great lengths to suggest we deal only with "reputable clinicians" and "credible" support groups, stay in bed and rest (which one must do anyway) and, apparently, have an occasional glass of milk as recommended by the National Dairy Association. I wondered where the illegitimate research was being done and where we could find an incredible support group.

Clearly, there would be no help from the "reputable medics" in solving our problem. As far as CFS and perhaps other chronic illness were concerned, they had no answers. If we had to work our way through a long list of alternative (read disreputable) therapies like wheatgrass juice, IV vitamins, and IV ozone, then we were ready to do it. The big question was—what next?

Even though we lived in Ashland, the most liberal and new age small town in Oregon, my search for information was frustrating. This community of 17,000 offered the opportunity to experience many different types of new age or alternative therapies. There was even a *Directory of Natural Choices* published by a self-styled "Chamber of Consciousness" which listed advertising blurbs for, among other things, acupuncture, art therapy, astrology, biofeedback, channeling, chiropractic, crystals, colonics, dream work, energy balancing, massage and bodywork, mercury-free dentistry, mineral baths, naturopathic physicians, oriental medicine, personal growth, psychic readings, Reiki, and reflexology. Some of the ads were quite provocative:

"Compassionate, expansive, high vibrational spirit guides bring their clarity and insightful assistance to personal readings and group channelings."

"Rebirthing is a conscious, connected breathing process for self-healing."

"Allow yourself the gift of Reiki."

"Enjoy better health with the world's most nutritious food—Super Blue-Green Algae."

"Multidimensional modalities for physical, mental, emotional and spiritual issues: psychic assessment. . .Reiki, tuning forks, color energy therapy, radionics."

I didn't know what most of this stuff was, but I intended to find out. I knew that Ashland had a tradition as a healing center. A friend had once told us that the local Indians—the Takelmas and Shastas—had come to the mineral springs in the Bear Creek Valley which spread below us and that the hillside where we resided was considered a healing place. That we were in a healing place remained arguable in Linda's mind. She had been ill since we had moved to Ashland and now she was feeling poorly again. After two weeks away, she was convinced there was something in the house that was making her ill.

"We may have to move," she said. "It could be the carpet or mold or dust from the basement or asbestos."

We were in a healing place and couldn't find healing. Therapies in the *Directory of Natural Choices* were virtually within walking distance, yet we knew not which path to follow next. Fifty years ago we could have walked around the corner and down the hill and seen a faith healer.

In the 1930s a thin, energetic, Christian lady named Susie Jessel arrived in town with a "healing gift." She was a cottage industry in Ashland for the next thirty years. Her treatment was simply the laying on of hands. She didn't charge for her work but only accepted what the patient could afford to pay. These were patients of last resort who had given up on the orthodox medical community and who, in many cases, had spent most of their money seeking cures. She treated tumors, shell-shock, heart conditions, diabetes, skin cancer, lung cancer, and other "incurable diseases," claiming an 80 percent success rate.

In 1943 an article in *True Magazine* brought people from all over the country to see Mrs. Jessel. Her husband built a treatment building and some small apartments and cabins on their property. These buildings are still there and look strangely out of place, unless one can visualize the hundreds of cars which lined these streets waiting to see Susie. During this period she treated four to five hundred people per day. Her success created animosity within both her Baptist church and the medical community. She was "read out" of the church, and she believed the local docs sicked the IRS on her. In 1954, the *Oregon Journal* printed a long article about her which brought a new influx of medical rejects, nearly overwhelming the ability of Ashland to house and feed them.

Susie saw her power as a normal thing, a gift from God. She was otherwise quite an ordinary person. She liked Ashland, helped people, and raised a large family. Today Ashland, in the tradition of Susie Jessel, is a center of holistic healing. Mrs. Jessel was not, however, a harbinger of the new age. She was a manifestation of the old-time religion.

We weren't quite ready for a faith healer, but we were pretty damn close.

At this time Linda had the following symptoms which I was tracking on a spreadsheet and rating on a scale of 1 (good) to 10 (bad). She was tired of repeatedly telling me where she felt bad so I made a checklist. Every other day or so I would read the symptoms to her and make her give me a number. The numbers might go up and down on a daily basis. Her chart in mid-October of 1993 showed the following:

Swollen left eye-3
Painful left cheekbone-2
Headache-5
Toothache-1
Sore throat-3
Swollen glands-3
Skin eruption on neck-1
Hair loss-5
Rash/sores on chest-1
Rash/sores on back-1
Gagging cough-6
Mucous in chest-6
Breathing difficulty-7
Chest pain-5
Muscle aches-8
Joint aches-9
Swollen fingers-10
Inflammation of fingers-7
Sleeplessness-0
Fatigue-8
Nausea-8
Loss of appetite-9
Rapid heartbeat-4
Bleeding gums-6
State of mind-7

Clearly, she was not having any fun. Each time she brushed her hair a large wad of the stuff would come out.

"I'm going to be bald," she stated.

"Of course you're not," I told her. But her hair was all over the bathroom. I had to call a plumber twice in one week to unplug our sewer line. He hauled a huge machine around the back of the house and put a cable with a small blade on the end down a vent pipe, started the motor, and chewed his way 100 feet through the pipe to the main sewer connection at the street.

"Man," he said from his rooftop vantage point. "You've got a spectacular view from up here."

"I know," I said. "But what's the problem with the pipe?"

"I think it's roots," he answered, staring off into the distance, taking in the town and the mountains and the sky. "You should build a viewing deck up here. This is great."

Two days later I called him back to ream it out again and enjoy the view. "You know," he told me. "It couldn't be roots this time. They don't grow that fast. Better check and see what people are stuffing down the toilet. Could be Kotex or something."

"How about hair?" I wondered.

"Could be hair. But it would take a lot of hair to stop this up in two days."

"I think it's hair," I told him. "I don't think you'll need to come back."

The next afternoon I began my career as a hair stylist. It was cold and crispy—a bright November afternoon. Linda had combed her long wet hair and it hung down the middle of her back.

"Just try and cut it straight," she instructed.

She watched me hold the scissors in her rearview mirror.

"Hurry up," she said. "It's cold."

"I don't want to make a mistake," I told her. I hesitated making the first move.

"What difference does it make?" she said.

I hacked it off at shoulder level. The thick hair fell in a pile on the patio. The cats sniffed at the hair then walked away.

"Is it even?" she wanted to know.

"It's so thick," I said.

"Not for long," said Linda, as I tried to even it up.

It had been a full year since she had noticed the bite on her eye. Linda's fiftieth birthday had passed unnoticed. This was at her request. She saw little to celebrate and was, as a matter of fact, steadily withdrawing from people, tired of being sick and of having her unwellness be her only topic of conversation. The falling hair didn't even seem to bother her that much. She was resigned. She brushed it out then cleaned out the sink, careful now not to flush it down the toilet.

"I'll be bald by Christmas," she stated.

"Oh no," I argued feebly. "I think I see some new hair coming in." But there was no denying that her thick, luxuriant mane of hair was gone and what remained was thin and wispy. She would get up in the middle of the night and snip at it with scissors, and in the morning or early afternoon when she rolled off the pillows she held between her aching knees and ankles she would look like the old TV comedian Professor Irwin Cory, with the scraggly ends of stiff and dry hair sticking up in the air.

It was, perhaps, inopportune to discuss the possibility of menopause with a newly fifty-year-old woman who was losing her hair, but my library and book shop research had led me to the conclusion that many of Linda's symptoms might be menopausal and could possibly exacerbate her many other problems. My sources included *The Silent Passage* by Gail Sheehy, who pointed out very clearly that menopause is a natural process. Ms. Sheehy then bogs down in a long argument over the role of estrogen, which ends in a guarded recommendation for hormone replacement therapy—on the face of it, an unnatural solution to a natural physiological change.

Her chapter on "Natural Menopause," however, caught my attention and encouraged me to study more on that subject. Ms. Sheehy's discussion of natural medicine vis-à-vis the change of life unfortunately ended with a little story about the horrible shrinking vagina. "But as estrogen levels decline, the vaginal tissues become thinner and drier. Gradually, over the decade of menopause, the vagina will shrink in both length and width. In many women of sixty who have taken no estrogen, I can hardly insert my pinkie," said the gynecologist." I didn't read this to Linda. With falling hair and a potential shrinking vagina to look forward to, it would be progressively more difficult, as the song says, to enjoy being a girl.

Ms. Sheehy's short chapter on alternative therapies led me to a book called, *Menopausal Years: The Wise Woman Way*, by Susan B. Weed, a herbalist. This is a five-star book, not only for its information on menopause, but on herbalism and healing in general. Ms. Weed suggests an eight-step process of healing which begins "with the least possible side effects and danger and ends with the most invasive." Hers was a truly holistic view: ". . .real healing can and does take place without the aid of drugs and surgery." Ms. Weed's steps provided us a new approach on how to approach illness, and I paraphrase her model as follows:

Step 1: "Do Nothing"
Resting, meditating, withdrawing.

Step 2: "Collect information"
Obtain diagnosis read books, join support groups.

Step 3: "Engage the energy"
Use crystals, homeopathy, prayer, color, aromatherapy.

Step 4: "Nourish and tonify"
Herbal infusions and tinctures, physical activity, life-style changes.

Step 5: "Stimulate/Sedate"
Massage, acupuncture, hydrotherapy, stronger herbal tinctures.

Step 6: "Use Supplements"
Vitamins and minerals, special foods.

Step 7: "Use drugs"
Synthetic pharmaceuticals and high-dilution homeopathics.

Step 8: "Break and enter"
Colonics, mammograms, biopsies, surgery, rolfing, psychoactive drugs.

Susan Weed's methodology is to move up a step at a time, carefully trying techniques and remedies until the problem is resolved, then moving back down through the steps until resting at Step 1.

Using her model, Linda and I had been all over the board. We had started at Step 7 with drugs, moved down to Step 5 with massage and acupuncture, gone to Step 8 with colonics and Step 6 with supplements, when we hadn't even really had a diagnosis at Step 2. We were flying blind, experimenting. The wise way seemed to be to back off from the higher-risk activities and go back to zero. But doing nothing is always the most difficult course. In addition, I knew very little about most of the techniques she outlined, such as homeopathy, aromatherapy, herbs, supplements, crystals, color, etc. This knowledge deficiency was soon to be remedied.

Chapter 11
Vibrational Healing

Our friend Joyce called. She wanted to know how Linda was doing. I knew that Joyce had recently recovered from a long illness. She asked if she could come over and bring Linda a healing toy.

"That sounds interesting," I said.

"Do you have any Rescue Remedy?" Joyce wanted to know.

"What's that?" I responded.

"Guess you don't, then," said Joyce. "I'll bring some."

When she arrived she brought a little bottle labeled "Nature's Rescue," a book, and two sets of copper screens which were hooked together with copper wire. There were four screens in each set—two big screens and two small ones. The small screens had strips of cloth sewn across them like a handle. The screens were made of copper mesh with a cloth border.

"Here's what you do," she told us. "One of the screens, the big one, goes behind your neck. The other large one goes under the small of your back."

"How?" I asked.

"You lie down on them. Put the big one on your pillow and position the other big one right under the small of your back. Then slip your hands through the straps of the small ones. Cross your ankles and you'll create a circuit with your body's own energy."

There was a small bottle in the middle of one of the connecting wires. The wires dead-ended into the little bottle which had a removable top.

"So, what's this bottle for?" I wondered.

"Put some pure water in the bottle and a drop of some medicine or remedy you're using. You could use Nature's Rescue, for example," she said holding up the blue bottle. "The essence of the remedy will be introduced into the circuit."

"What are these circuits going to do?" I asked.

Joyce handed me a book. "This will tell you everything. But

briefly, creating the circuit will help balance your energy. It will remove or help to remove blockages to energy movement. You'll find it's very relaxing. It will help Linda get rest and she needs rest to heal. You can experiment with the bottle. Try different things. Try herbs or vitamins or even aspirin. It works better if you also take the substance internally."

"Okay," I said. "But what's Rescue Remedy?"

"Have you heard of Bach Flower Remedies?" Joyce asked.

"I've heard of them and seen them at the food store, but I don't know what they are. What are they?"

"There's lots of books on that, too," said Joyce. "When Linda's depressed or weepy or upset, put a few drops under her tongue and see what it does."

"You know a lot about this stuff, don't you?"

"I've tried lots of different things," she told me.

"What else?" I wanted to know.

"This is enough for now," she said. "I'll call in a couple of days. Try these things out and see what you think."

I had watched Linda experience many therapies but here was one I was going to get to try out. I decided to give it an immediate test drive and arranged the screens as instructed, lowered myself onto them, slipped my hands through the straps, crossed my ankles, and waited. I was surprised to notice that after a very short time I felt a tingling feeling in my feet and hands. Pinpoint spots on my face began to itch intensely, requiring immediate scratching. A short time later, perhaps twenty minutes, I awoke from a dreamless sleep feeling calm and collected—balanced, if you will. It seemed time to break the circuit, and I uncrossed my legs and removed my hands.

"You were really snoring," said Linda, who had been resting beside me on the bed. "Big snoring noises. Awful noises."

She loved to provide excruciatingly detailed commentaries on snoring. She was almost a student of snoring.

"I didn't know I was asleep," I said.

"No one knows they're asleep, do they?" she replied.

"I mean I wasn't aware that I was going to sleep. I wasn't sleepy. I was lying there trying to feel something, some energy or something, and the next thing I knew I woke up."

"That's called a nap," said Linda.

"What I mean is, I didn't think I needed a nap. I wasn't sleepy. But when I got into these things I went right to sleep."

"It relaxed you," she said.

"You should try it," I told her.

"I don't want to right now," she said.

"You should," I persisted.

"Not now," said Linda. " I don't have the energy to make a circuit."

The book Joyce left me was called *Biocircuits: Amazing New Tools For Energy Health* by Leslie Patten. Ms. Patten wrote that these screens, or biocircuits, were the invention of a WWI Royal Flying Corps pilot named Leon Eeman, who had crashed his plane in 1915 and was later, as a result of complications from injuries, declared 100 percent disabled. Believing that allopathic medicine had failed him, and feeling that he couldn't live much longer, he decided to find his own method of recovery. After study and observation Eeman concluded that: "Human beings radiate energy, and this energy radiates more powerfully or accumulates more readily in specific areas of the body. These locations can be linked together to create a circuit that enhances recuperative processes and produces a flow of energy–the energy of life. It alone is the power that heals. In addition, this energy can be transferred, or conducted between individuals. This may occur naturally, as when lovers embrace, or intentionally, as when healers use their hands."

I had never really thought much about the nature of human energy, or vital force as designated by the naturopaths before my experience with the Eeman screens, or relaxation circuit, as he called it. I lived almost totally in the physical world with intermittent attempts at meditation. And even in meditation my experience was preoccupied with the physical. Qigong had begun to provide some insights into energy movement through and around the body and, though I could make no great claims to feeling ch'i, I thought I was starting to sense some awareness of energy coursing through my limbs. Skeptical, as always, I realized that this could be a self-fulfilling prophecy. There was one thing for certain about Qigong–I had a significantly increased tolerance to cold. If heat was evidence of energy, I was producing more of it. No longer would I pull on a down parka when the temperature hit forty degrees. On many cold days I was forsaking a jacket entirely. The screens, however, provided immediate energy feedback. I could feel it—whatever "it" was.

As a child I had a visualization of the soul which I had been taught vitalized the body, giving life. My image of the soul had always been a spot somewhere inside my head. But the streaming of sensation through my hands and feet while lying on the relaxation circuit began to broaden my concept of vitalizing energy. It now seemed to be something like electricity or magnetism flowing through and around the body in patterns like blood flowing in the cellular body.

Our kids, brought up on *Star Wars*, talked about "the force." On public television shows, Tai Chi masters used their force to move physical objects. It seemed possible that with understanding, training, and concentration, or even by virtue of some gift or talent, one could begin to manage this energy, force, soul power, or ch'i and use it for one's own benefit or the benefit of others. It was difficult, but not impossible, for me to believe that the human body could radiate a field of energy which was invisible to the naked eye. It was likewise difficult, but possible, to believe that certain people, as I later read, claimed to be able to see these energy fields—alleged they could see the shape and color. I doubted that my own sensitivity could ever increase to a point where I could see energy. But then, I couldn't see the wind either, though I could sense it physically and observe its results. I could also feel heat from my body and from other people's bodies. In fact, I recognized that since I had been regularly practicing Qigong exercise, I could feel the heat from other walkers when I passed them on the street. I understood also that energy is not peripheral to our vocabulary: "She has lots of energy." "He has good energy." "I like his energy." "The group has a good energy." "I have low energy today." Energy was a word we used often and apparently knew little about.

Eeman discovered that by linking the base and top of the spine to the hands using his relaxation circuit he could produce warmth, relaxation, and energy movement. In 1922 he set up a consulting practice in London and worked until his death in 1958. He performed many experiments to gain validation from the medical community. He treated a variety of disorders during his thirty-five years of practice, including rheumatism, digestive and respiratory disorders, headaches, sciatica, and many others with apparently good results.

These were often achieved by creating a circuit between two or more people during which energy from well people was transmitted to those unwell—a wired-up laying on of hands.

After several years of experience he posited that the human body had polarity along several axes, which accounted for energy flow from head to feet, from right to left, and from back to front.

Eeman had his best results with insomnia. I could certainly vouch for the fact that using the screens quickly put me to sleep. Linda's experiences were less pleasant, and there appeared to be major energy blockages in her hands and feet caused by arthritis. Using the relaxation circuit would tend to increase the pain in her hands and feet, and she was reluctant to use them. My experiences were positive, pleasant and, therefore, frequent. The Eeman screens, relaxation circuits, or biocircuits—whatever you wanted to call them—increased my level of understanding of the body's energy. I called Joyce to ask how long I could keep the biocircuits.

"Keep them as long as you want," she said. "We're using silk ones."

"Are they better than copper?" I asked.

"More subtle; less intense," she replied.

"Where can I get some?" I wanted to know.

Joyce referred me to the book on biocircuits I'd been reading. "I think there's some information in the back on how you can order some. But be patient. Maybe I'll find time to make you a set of silk ones."

If the screens didn't immediately suit Linda, Bach's Rescue Remedy was a complete winner. Whenever she seemed overwrought, or was weepy, I'd run for the bottle and drop three or four drops of liquid under her tongue. The effect was always immediate. It calmed her and balanced her emotions. In the next six months I bought three bottles of the stuff. One to return to Joyce and the other two for Linda. I used it once or twice myself and gave it to the cats as well. The owner of All's Well, the health food store where I made my purchase, told me that he couldn't have raised his kids without it.

Edward Bach, another Englishman, was a practitioner of orthodox medicine who then switched to homeopathy. He was a pathologist and bacteriologist who developed a type of vaccine which is still used by many homeopaths. In 1930 he quit his

London practice and moved to the English countryside with the goal of developing a new system of healing. A few years earlier on a visit to Wales, he had picked some wildflowers which he later prepared homeopathically and used in his clinic with excellent results. He wanted to develop a healing method so simple that anyone could use it. His short book, *Heal Thyself*, first published in 1931, is a masterpiece.

Bach believed "the main reason for the failure of modern medical science is that it is dealing with results and not causes." Bach wanted to attack disease at its origin. He clearly demonstrated a spiritual predisposition when he wrote, "Disease in its origin is not material." "Disease," he said, "is in essence the result of conflict between Soul and Mind, and will never be eradicated except by spiritual and mental effort. No effort directed at the body alone can do more than superficially repair damage." Dr. Bach insisted that to understand the nature of disease, one had to acknowledge five fundamental truths:

1. Man has a soul which is our real self and which is a reflection of God.

2. We are in the world to gain knowledge and experience for the purpose of advancing the perfection of our natures.

3. Our life on earth is but a brief moment in the evolution of our soul; our body being only a vehicle for our soul's progress through the world.

4. When our personalities are led astray by our own desires or the influence of others, conflicts with the soul arise; and this conflict is the root cause of unhappiness and disease.

5. We are part of the Creator, and because of the unity of all things, any action we take affects the whole.

Thus, there were two fundamental errors: "disassociation between our souls and our personalities, and cruelty or wrong to others, for this is a sin against unity." A sin against unity equaled conflict, and this conflict would ultimately manifest as disease.

If life is a learning experience and disease is the result of deviations from the path of the soul, disease can be seen as beneficial for it helps put the personality back on track. Disease, in Dr. Bach's logic, is also avoidable and preventable, because if we can correct our mistakes, our deviations from the correct path, there is no need to learn the "lessons of suffering."

"The real primary diseases of men are such defects as pride, cruelty, hate, self-love, ignorance, instability, and greed." These faults are the real diseases, which lay behind our physical afflictions.

LINDA'S VOICE: *In a dream I'm Rip Van Winkle–but I'm not. I haven't been in a dead sleep all my life. I've learned lessons; I've changed. I wake up and look in the mirror. I'm old. Have I been like Rip? I want to look young. I want to start over with my lessons, with the things I know now, with the way I am now. But you can't go back; can't change your life. The mistakes–you acted on what you knew then.*

It is reported that Dr. Bach, as he walked under the flowering trees of the English countryside and through the fields of wildflowers which decorated the woods in spring, was so sensitive that by touching a drop of dew from the bloom to his lips he could intuit the problem which the flower essence could heal. If white chestnut depressed him, he knew that in homeopathic dilution it would ease depression, that wild oat could remove the blockages of uncertainty and allow a free flow of ideas.

I was ready to understand Dr. Bach, for the previous spring I had spent hours walking through the wildflowers and the blooming trees and shrubs. I had photographed a hundred species in the early mornings, my free time before Linda stirred, and I could easily visualize the clairvoyant doctor bending, reaching, and lightly touching a drop of dew from the flower to his lips, then perhaps sitting and waiting for its effects to manifest. To watch the flowers bloom is to know there is a power there. Dr. Bach was fortunate to be able to understand that power and interpret it for the rest of us.

Not being a scientist, I needed to run no long experiments. Bach's Rescue Remedy worked and worked consistently. It wasn't a panacea or a cure-all, but when emotions were out of balance, a few drops would create balance. We had tried many things which hadn't worked or which could not be validated as working. Rescue Remedy was, through anecdotal deduction, a product we would never be without.

A Bach Remedy is the essence of a flower in the maturity of full bloom. The flowers are carefully picked and put on the top of spring water in a clear bowl of glass or quartz. The bowl is left in the sun for a period of time and then the flowers are removed. A few drops of liquid from the bowl is mixed in a dropper bottle with water, along with a small amount of brandy as a preservative. Flower essences are similar to homeopathic remedies in that they contain only the essence of the original substance.

When I first read about the preparation of these remedies, I felt it was like alchemy. But I was sold on Dr. Bach and chose, for the time being, to suspend disbelief.

Most medical doctors believe that homeopathic preparations are alchemy. Homeopathy, I learned, actually has a longer history than the allopathic medicine which is currently predominate in our culture. In fact, homeopathy once had the upper hand, if not in numbers of physicians using the homeopathic method, at least in public support. Interestingly, and unknown to most Americans, homeopathy is widespread around the world. It is very popular in England, France, Germany, and India. Reportedly, 20,000 Indian doctors practice homeopathy.

Because of its worldwide popularity and due to a resurgence of interest in the United States, one could assume that homeopathic medicine works. The fact that the World Health Organization estimates that 500 million people around the world choose homeopathy is evidence, perhaps even scientific evidence, of its efficacy.

Homeopathy is a system of drug therapy devised by a German doctor named Hahnemann, who was born in 1755. On the face of it, homeopathy does sound a bit goofy. Hahnemann would give a chemical substance such as opium to a healthy person and then record the symptoms which developed. He noted that there were two distinct sets of symptoms. The first set he labeled "primary" and for opium, as an example, they were: "fearless elevation of spirit, a sensation of strength and high courage, an imaginative gaiety." However, after several hours a second set of symptoms developed—again in the case of opium: "relaxation of the body's vital force to the substance." To Hahnemann and his followers, this vital force was the reactive power of the body to external stimuli. In an illness situation, the reactive power shows up as symptoms. To a homeopathic practitioner, symptoms are the best guides to devising a treatment for disease. Unlike allopathic physicians, homeopaths do not try to suppress symptoms, believing that bodily reactions such as fever and skin eruptions are evidence of the vital force at work, attempting to throw off toxins or internal wastes. Thus, the homeopathic physician attempts to pick a medicine which supports the secondary symptoms, recognizing that symptoms are part of the body's healing effort.

By carefully noting the symptoms of a patient, the homeopath matches a very specific remedy to a very specific set of symptoms. Over the years homeopaths have "proved" more than 2,000 remedies. The proving is done by giving the chemical or substance to healthy people and recording their reactions. These primary reactions are listed by each "proved" substance in the *materia medicas* (compendiums of remedies) of homeopathy. When the set of symptoms match perfectly, that drug is given. This is known as the Law of Similars. A homeopathic physician—and there are a few medical doctors again practicing homeopathy—uses nearly a thousand medicines in his or her practice. Compare this to allopaths who work with only a few medicines day to day.

After discovering the Law of Similars, Hahnemann came up with a second rule—The Minimum Dose. Somehow he figured out that if he reduced the dose substantially, the primary symptoms were mitigated and the secondary symptoms remained unimpaired. Those secondary symptoms represented the curative effect—the reaction of the body's vital force, its attempt to get well. Thus, homeopathic drugs enhance the natural healing disposition of the body, which then wipes out whatever disorder in the vital force exists.

At this point in my understanding, I could begin to see the conflict between homeopaths and allopaths. The allopath believes that illness is caused by a germ or virus and that a symptom is like a wound caused by this outside force. The germ or virus or disorder is seen by the allopath as an entity, and groups of symptoms are patterned into groups of diseases. Thus, the allopathic view is quite static. The allopath will say you have flu, cold, bronchitis, pneumonia, allergy, heart disease, Parkinson's, multiple sclerosis, cancer, etc. We know all the allopathic categories. But the homeopath allows for individualization. In the homeopathic view there are 2,000 or more "diseases." There are too many to name. Hahnemann called them by the medicine which cured them. With homeopathy mental symptoms are included. These symptoms are considered very important. For the homeopath there is no difference between physical and mental illness. There is no departmentalization as in allopathy. Remember that Dr. Bach was a homeopath, and he believed that the root cause of disease was mental.

The preparation of homeopathic medicines is what causes most allopaths to howl with laughter. Homeopathic medicines are so diluted that in many preparations there is not a single molecule of the original substance remaining! It is only in dilution that the secondary or curative symptoms are stimulated. Even more interesting is that homeopaths believe that the more the remedy is diluted, the more potent it is. Allopaths cry, "placebo," but can 500 million users of homeopathic medicines be that wrong?

In our own country homeopathy had quite a run in the second half of the nineteenth century. The first homeopaths were referred to as "German quacks" by the allopathic community, who over time lost many patients to homeopathic practice. The acceptance of homeopathy, which coincided with the rise of herbal doctors, was perhaps a reaction to the overuse of allopathic drugs like mercury and other practices that seem barbarous in retrospect. Clergymen, in particular, were attracted to homeopathy, perhaps by the spiritual essence of the medicine. Women were impressed with the kinder treatment of children by homeopathic doctors. Domestic kits which gave detailed instructions for self-dosing were marketed and were popular. The real problem for the allopaths was that the homeopaths were making more money and, to counter the growth of homeopathy in the United States, the American Medical Association was formed. The history of that struggle is documented in great detail by Harris L. Coulter in *Divided Legacy: The Conflict Between Homeopathy and The American Medical Association.*

Significant in the downfall of American homeopathy was the strictness of its rules. A true Hahnemannian did not vary from The Law of Similars, The Minimum Dose, and The Single Remedy. (Hahnemann's third rule says that only one drug should be given at a time.) The law of The Single Remedy caused a split among homeopaths, some of whom used multiple doses or even combinations. When the homeopaths began to argue among themselves, they were easier prey for the AMA.

Constantine Hering, a strict Hahnemann disciple, also known as the father of American homeopathy, died in 1880 in the middle of the conflict. He devised Hering's Law, which postulates that symptoms disappear in the reverse order of their appearance as healing takes place.

My brother Bart had described Hering's law to me many years before, although chiropractors refer to it as "retracing." They believe, as do naturopaths, that when healing is taking place, symptoms will repeat themselves in reverse chronological order, retracing their path through the body and the mind. This means that when one is getting well there may be a healing crisis—a reoccurrence of old symptoms. Hering further stated that these symptoms would move in specific directions: from more vital to less vital, from the interior of the body to the skin and from the top downward. This is one of the reasons holistic practitioners believe that skin ailments are generally a good sign. The body is moving toxins away from vital organs. In a true healing experience symptoms from old diseases which had been suppressed by improper treatment could reappear.

I still didn't know why homeopathy worked, but I did understand how it worked. The problem was where to find a Hahnemann or a Hering. The closest we had come so far was Herxheimer and his damn die-off reaction. The Community Food Store did sell homeopathic remedies. They all seemed to be combination remedies rather than a single remedy. I bought the one marked "Asthma" for Linda's breathing problem and another for "Arthritis." The "Asthma" included homeopathic lobelia and had some effect, although it didn't work as well as the herbal tincture. The homeopathic arthritis formula didn't work at all. But from my reading of the Hahnemannian method, it seemed that picking a remedy off a shelf based on an allopathic disease description was not a true homeopathic approach. I liked what I had learned but didn't know how to follow up.

Chapter 12
Multilevel Marketing

By this time we were beginning to get all kinds of suggestions. A friend of Linda's she hadn't heard from in twenty years somehow learned she was ill and called to tell us about a special concoction of chromium picolinate blended with herbs, which was supposed to specifically give a boost to sufferers of CFS. I called the number her friend gave me and talked to the man who was selling the product. The salesman was a registered nurse married to a surgeon. He told me he had been in bed for a year until he began to take the chromium, which gave him an energy boost and got him on his feet. I sent him $30 and Linda began to take that remedy.

The product received was called the "Herbal Energizer," a combination of chromium picolinate and twelve herbs. Chromium picolinate has received much publicity as an aid to weight loss. The literature which arrived with Herbal Energizer reported double-blind studies which show that in a six-week period subjects lost 23 percent or 4.4 pounds of fat without changing dietary or exercise habits. Herbs in the mixture such as ephedra and guavana boost energy while rehmania root and reishi mushroom strengthen the immune system. The reishi supposedly aids the body's efforts to produce interferon, which is a protein produced in our own cells to fight viral infections. The Herbal Energizer sounded great. Unfortunately, there was no apparent result for Linda.

This was an introduction to the world of multilevel marketing, which in the field of health-related products levels its guns at sufferers of chronic illness.

I had been a salesman for a very long time and, though I did not consider myself a great salesperson, I was good enough to know that a referral with a testimonial attached is the most powerful sales pitch there is. The referral and the testimonial are the keys to the unbelievable success of multilevel marketing. By now, almost everyone in America has at least one sales kit from a multilevel marketing organization. In case you've been missed by Amway, Shaklee, Herbal Life, Mannatech, Sunrider, Reliv, KM, Life Force, or one of the many companies marketing products in this manner, here's how they work: a friend or relative has the occasion to speak with you about the wonderful new product(s) they've been using. In the case of health-related products, they will attest to how the products have changed their life and given them energy they haven't had since they were small children. They will offer you samples or material about the product and encourage you to give it a try. If you demonstrate a passing interest, they will point out that you can build a business out of your home by using and selling these products to your own circle of friends and acquaintances with, in most cases, no initial investment other than the $30 to $40 annual distributor's fee. If you pay the distributor's fee you can buy the products for your own use at a 20-30 percent discount. If you sign up more distributors under you and create a new level of sales people, this becomes your "downline," and you get a commission on their sales. As the sales volume of your downline increases, your discounts and rewards increase, as do those of the friend who signed you up in the first place—your "upline." The companies grow as the downlines are built one level at a time, creating a vast pyramidal chart with a handful of people at the top becoming very wealthy and a large group at the upper middle of the pyramid doing quite well. It is a brilliant product distribution scheme which has been used effectively with products as diverse as life insurance.

Health-related products, like personal care products, seem to do quite well in the multilevel scheme. From a corporate standpoint, it allows a manufacturer to move product without a paid sales force. No real estate is necessary, and training costs are minimal. The marketing effort consists of building and maintaining a high level of enthusiasm out there in the field by making certain that uplines stay in contact with downlines, holding frequent conferences and meetings, and awarding highly-publicized bonuses for those who are making greater than normal sales.

It has always amazed me that someone can try something for a very short period of time and then tout it as a panacea to anyone who will listen. I've done it myself. I still do it myself. It must be that we are looking for confirmation of a hypothesis. Or, it may be that we want to make money and are quite willing to make claims that we only hope are true.

Linda's old friend, the one who located Herbal Energizer for us, called a couple weeks later. He'd seen an ad in the *Portland Business Review* which simply said "Chronic Fatigue" and had a phone number. He had called and talked to a woman who told him about a series of products which she was convinced had cured her chronic fatigue. He gave me the number and I picked up the phone again.

Needless to say, at this point in our adventure we were extremely discouraged. We were open to suggestions and were willing to throw some money at the problem. We were, in fact, eager to listen to the referral with testimonial.

The woman I called was named Lila. She introduced me to a line of products manufactured by a company named Reliv. I had never heard of Reliv, but Lila explained in her quiet but professional way that Reliv had been formed by a retired insurance executive ("like you," said Lila) who wanted to create the perfect company. He linked up with a scientist who had invented a formulation of vitamins, herbs, and minerals which was the first patented product of its type. These vitamins came in a powder and could be mixed in juice or water and taken two to three times a day. In addition, Reliv had an energy-building product and a colon cleanser, all in powdered form. These three products could also be purchased in bars to be eaten as a snack.

"They've really changed my life," she told me. "I used to have to put my head down on my desk at work and just sleep for an hour. Now I have energy to burn. My husband has quit his job, and we're making this our full-time business."

I was having visions of a second career myself. I believed in vitamins. I agreed with Lila that our food supply, grown in overworked and chemically-laden soil was no doubt depleted of the essentials which had formerly made it so fertile. I believed also that our own exposure to chemicals and toxins had reduced our bodies' ability to completely and entirely process the nutrients in our food. I had read somewhere that our bodies were no longer as efficient in producing enzymes necessary for digestion as they had once been. Thus, it didn't take much to convince me that a powdered vitamin and energy drink could give Linda the boost she needed to set her on the path to wellness.

"The powder is easier for the body to assimilate," Lila told me.

"A friend who's in the septic tank business told me he sees lots of tanks that are full of undigested vitamin tablets."

"My God," I exclaimed.

I ordered some Reliv Classic and some Energizer. I paid full retail, as Lila wasn't pushing the business opportunity at me.

"I'll send this out today, and I'll call you in two or three days to see how your wife is doing. I really want to talk to her. I know how bad it can be to want to stay in bed all the time."

Eighty or ninety dollars for a few cans of vitamins and supplements was a small price to pay. I needed something to boost Linda's morale and mine too. The chromium had been a bust, compared with the testimonials of the marketer. I was convinced Reliv would help. I was actually ready to tout before I'd tasted. Lila was going to send me names and phone numbers of other people who had suffered from various diseases and who would attest that Reliv had helped. Testimonials by the page! If I had had a page full of insurance clients testify on my behalf, I would have made a lot more money in the old insurance biz. Wouldn't it be great, I thought, to sell something that people could get excited about? I was ready to get on the phone and start calling people to tell them what a great product Reliv was. I reflected back to the ladies from Bellevue who had almost insisted that I sell Sunrider. I realized suddenly that we had a whole box of Sunrider in the cupboard. I carried the box of Sunrider into the bedroom.

"Where'd this come from?" I asked Linda who was lying on her back looking at the ceiling.

"I bought it from a friend," she said, closing her eyes. "I took some but I forgot about it. I'm also supposed to drink Cali tea. I've got a box of that somewhere."

While I was waiting for Reliv, I decided to make Linda some Sunrider. The problem was that she was hardly eating. Most foods made her nauseous. I tried Sunrider, soy milk, and a banana. I ended up drinking that. Since she was craving ice cream, which I refused to buy because of its sugar content, I blended the Sunrider, which came in different fruit flavors, with yogurt and froze it. During the course of a day she would manage to eat the frozen treat.

The Reliv arrived with marketing material that was extremely professional. "Nourish the World" was the company's slogan and they seemed serious. The art work on the cans was snazzy, the photography in the brochures first-class. Clearly, Reliv was a company one could be proud to be associated with. I'd signed up for multilevel marketing distributorships in past years. I had a sales kit from Shaklee and one from a company that sold bee pollen. I became a bee pollen distributor in an attempt to stay in good favor with a large commercial insurance client, proving that prostitution comes in many forms. When the client lost interest in bee pollen, so did I, and it took me a couple of years to nibble away at the large supply of bee pollen granules that had accumulated in the refrigerator. Bee pollen, as with Reliv, KM, Sunrider, Herbalife, and others, was supposed to enhance one's level of energy, tweak the immune system, and aid the body in fighting or casting off disease. The only thing I know for sure is that the bee pollen got chewier as it aged.

For several weeks I mixed vitamin shakes and energy drinks for Linda, blending them with a variety of liquids to increase their palatability. She didn't like them and would struggle to finish a glass. I thought they tasted okay. I knew nothing tasted good to her. Linda was hopeful they would help and worked hard trying to finish them. I was excited about Reliv. It's easy to sell a salesman—we honor a good pitch.

Lila actually did call a few days later.

"Did the product arrive?" she wanted to know. She always referred to it as "the product." All multilevel marketing people refer to their vitamins and supplements as "the product."

"Yes," I said. "We've been taking it for several days now."

"I'm sorry I haven't called sooner. I was down in Boise for a few days meeting with my downline distributors. There are some really exciting things going on now with the company. This company is really starting to move. How's your wife feeling? How does she like the product?"

"Well," I told her. "The problem is that she's so nauseous all the time that she doesn't like the taste of anything."

"I know how she feels. I've been there," said Lila. "She just needs to keep taking it. There are digestive enzymes in the formula which will help her stomach feel better. Is she up? Can I speak with her?"

"She's asleep," I replied. "Sorry."

"I'll call back in a week," said Lila. "You know," she continued. "I wish you'd listen to our conference call on Thursday night."

"What's the conference call?"

"Every Thursday we have a thirty-minute call when distributors call in and talk about the product and how they're doing. This week it's going to be all doctors and dentists."

"Medical docs are selling Reliv!" I exclaimed. This was an exciting concept.

"Do you want to hear the call?" she asked.

"Yeah," I said. "I really do."

"I'll call you at 6:30 P.M. on Thursday and patch you in," said Lila.

Doctors? Doctors selling this stuff as multiline distributors? I called my stockbroker.

"What's the deal on a company called Reliv?" I asked.

I could hear him punching some buttons on his computer terminal. After a minute he said, "It's on the American Stock Exchange. Initial public offering was last year. Opened at thirteen and promptly dropped to the four to five level. It's trading now about five. We don't have any research on it. It's pretty small. The analysts don't start watching these companies until their sales reach $100 million. Looks like they're at about $50 million. Hey! This is kind of interesting."

"What?"

"A high percentage of their sales are coming from overseas. Mexico and Australia. What do you know about it?"

"Not much," I told him. "I've got some of the product. Great marketing materials. It's patented, if that means anything. Apparently, though, they've got lots of docs interested. If docs start pushing it, it could be big."

"How much you want?" he asked.

Feeling aggressive, I ordered a thousand shares.

"Hey," said the stockbroker, "You ever tried KM?"

"Heard of it," I told him, "But, no, I never have."

"It's great. Gives me tremendous energy. Haven't had so much energy since I was a little kid. You should try it."

"Are you a distributor?"

"Sure," he said, "You get a discount when you're a distributor."

"Sell very much?"

"Not enough to make a living," he replied. "I sell it to family members and close friends. A few clients use it too. I'll send you a brochure. It's a special formulation of fourteen herbs. It was formulated by a Swiss doctor. They say the formula came to him in a dream."

"The same way you get your stock picks. I can see why you're attracted."

"Come on. Be nice. We're making a little money," he said a bit defensively.

"How much is this stuff?" I asked.

"It's forty bucks a bottle. Of course, if you're a distributor you get a 20 percent discount."

"Of course. That's the way multilevel marketing works. It's pretty much like a Ponzi scheme," I said.

"Jeeze, don't say that to any of these multilevel marketing types. They are really sensitive if you say 'pyramid' at them."

"Too sensitive, don't you think?" I wanted to know.

"You've got to wonder," said the stockbroker. The markup on all this stuff like KM is huge. I mean if you make it to the highest level of any of these plans—which means about five levels of distribution in your downline—you're going to be getting a 40 to 50 percent commission. What was your average commission when you were selling insurance?"

"About 14 percent."

"Well, mine is less than that."

"That's why you're churning everyone's portfolio," I said.

"You are in a nasty mood today," said the stockbroker. "What I'm saying is that a bottle of KM, if they sold it in a health food store, probably would go for twenty-five bucks. I guess the theory is you can move a lot more product with 100,000 salespeople and for no great cost, since you're charging them $30 a year for the opportunity to sell the stuff." He paused. "Wait a minute. If a multiline company has 100,000 distributors, and they each pay an annual distributor's fee of $30, that's $3 million a year! It's brilliant. Your sales force, instead of being a constant pain in the butt, padding their expense accounts, wanting a nicer car, begging for a cell phone. . .your sales force is a profit center. The guy who thought this up should get the Nobel Prize for business."

"There is no Nobel Prize for business," I told him.

"Maybe I should buy some of this Reliv stock. Do you think I should?" he asked.

"You're the damn stockbroker," I exclaimed.

"Yes, I am," he said. "And you've wasted my time long enough this morning. I've got other, richer, nicer, more important people holding to talk to me."

"Okay," I said. "Good-bye."

"Wait!" he shouted. "You're not doing anything. Find a product and we can start a multiline company. We could be rich. There's got to be something out there we can put through the old pyramid. How about that blue-green algae?"

"They're doing it."

"Soap?"

"Amway."

"More herbs?"

"Herbalife."

"Say," he said, "I've noticed the big mutual funds are buying Herbalife. You want me to look into it for you?"

"No, I don't."

"How about life insurance?"

"A.L. Williams."

"We're too late. I'm always too late. I could have bought Microsoft at twelve. No vision."

"Good-bye," I said, hanging up the phone.

I tuned into the Thursday conference call and was impressed by the enthusiasm of the doctors discussing the importance of nutrition and supplementation. They all seemed to like the fact that Reliv products were easy to take, which guaranteed patient compliance. The fact that Reliv came in powdered form led several to the conclusion it was absorbed more easily than tablets or capsules. A surgeon from South Carolina said, "Patients love the taste, so there's no problem getting them to take it." An M.D. from Tennessee reported reduction in blood pressure and cholesterol levels in patients on Reliv. "Individuals with diabetes, hypoglycemia, fatigue, and other medical conditions have improved with less use of prescription medicines," she said. A family practitioner from Houston related that "eight out of ten of my patients experience increased energy and an improved sense of well-being. The more I recommend it, the more I see improvements in aches and pains." A pediatrician from Ohio announced with authority that "Reliv products are the finest nutritional supplements I've ever seen."

Reliv's marketing department was on the ball. Using docs to move products was the key to the success of the pharmaceutical industry. I was more excited by the company than I was the product at this point.

Lila did send me a list of people who were apparently willing to attest that Reliv had helped them with surgery recovery, hypoglycemia, vertigo, sugar addiction, colitis, skin problems, colon problems, leg ulcers, asthma, allergies, cancer recovery, sinus infection, chronic fatigue, candida, depression, acne, fibrocystic lumps, migraines, diabetes, lactose intolerance, thyroid, psoriasis, lupus, Parkinson's, jungle rot, PMS, arthritis, leg cramps, and MS. Many of the ailments on the list had more than one contact. Clearly, the distributors of Reliv believed that a fat, unhealthy, undernourished society needed these products. Reliv's mission to "Nourish the World" had a three-pronged approach:

"1. Reliv offers a line of products the world wants and needs. Faced with rising health care costs and a growing sense of their own mortality, Americans increasingly look for ways to stay healthier longer.

"2. The company is determined to make a profound difference in the world's nutritional health. Reliv focuses on introducing products into countries where people from all walks of life seek optimal health and financial opportunity.

"3. Most importantly, Reliv offers a simple, fair, and equitable five-tier compensation plan that yields exponential rewards for hard work."

Reliv soon became concerned about the world's skin condition as they introduced a line of beauty products. The biggest concern I had about my Reliv investment was—can anyone afford to use it? For example, I would buy a can of the flagship product, Reliv Classic, for $20 with my 25 percent distributor's discount. There were twenty servings in a can of classic which contains vitamins, trace minerals, essential amino acids, and some herbs. Classic, then would cost us $1 per day; $2 a day if I also took it. The cost per day of Energize, Reliv's isotonic sports (energy) drink, with two servings a day recommended, was also $1 per day or $2 if I took it as well. Fibrestore, a high-fiber product to keep those bowels moving at a high level of efficiency, was also approximately $1 per serving, or $2 for two people. Thus, if we took all three products each day, our cost per month at a 25 percent discount from retail would be $180.

In the insurance business we used to say, "If the price is too high, the value is too low." And as Dr. Jensen always says, "If you don't spend it on good food, you'll spend it later on the doctor." The cost of good health appears high on the short term. I decided to consider it insurance and paid the premium. Many people, I rationalized, must spend $180 per month on alcohol and cigarettes. We would give Reliv a chance and, at the same time, watch that stock go up.

The problem was the stock immediately began to drop. First to $4.00, then to $3.00 and, finally, to $2.50 per share. On paper I had lost $2,500! Since I had spent more than $500 on Reliv products, I was in very deep. What Lila had failed to tell me was that Reliv's manufacturing plant was in a flood plain and had been inundated by the big floods of 1993. The retired insurance (like myself) executive who had started Reliv had apparently forgotten to, or opted not to, purchase flood insurance. Equipment and raw materials had been saved but the plant had to relocate temporarily to high ground. Product was moving but the flood would affect profitability in 1993, causing the stock to drop dramatically. I decided to ride it out. What else could I do?

Chapter 13
Cleaning House

It was late November, 1993. Linda had seen no practitioner of the healing arts for a month. She lay in bed trying to get well. She hurt. She ached. She slept poorly, if at all. She was cold. She had no appetite. Her hair continued to land in the sink. She tried to take the powdered vitamin and energy supplements but could never finish a glassful. Food smelled bad. She cried and I put Rescue Remedy under her tongue. Occasionally, she would wander into the backyard and sit on a bench with her back against the fence to soak up some sun. She worried that there were molds and fungus in the house which were poisoning her. She was concerned that asbestos was blowing through the heating vents and filling her lungs with harmful microscopic particles. She wanted the carpet removed, fearing that it was exhaling dust into her tender respiratory track. She talked about moving to Arizona, Hawaii, and even Tahiti. She was uncomfortable using the relaxation circuits. They hurt her fingers.

LINDA'S VOICE: *A train is passing. Everyone I love is on a fast-moving flatbed. But it slows down so I can jump on. Someone reaches, extending their arm. I run and grab. They pull me aboard as the train speeds up. We're standing, hugging, happy. I have a good, tingly feeling. Someone throws a blanket over me and says, "Take care of yourself."*

I called Joyce. "Do you have any more tricks you haven't told us about?" I asked.

"You could have a dowser come in and check your house," she said.

"To look for water?" I wondered. I was confused.

"No, dowsers can find things other than water. In fact, a good one can answer lots of questions about health or harmful conditions in your home."

I didn't understand what she was talking about.

"How do they do it?" I wanted to know.

"They use a pendulum, normally," she told me.

"Can you do this?" I asked.

"I only do it for myself. I don't do it for other people."

"I just don't understand," I told her.

"When I move into a new place, I dowse it first to make sure there's no harmful radiations in the house."

"What if there are?"

"Then I won't move in," said Joyce. "I also dowse my food to make sure it's what I should be eating that day. I check vitamins, too. I can normally tell which I should take and how much I should take."

"The pendulum tells you this?"

"Look," said Joyce. "I really want to help. What I could do is dowse your place and tell Linda if there are things in the house which would keep me from being healthy there—like molds and fungus or whatever."

"That would be good," I told her.

Linda was excited when I told her that Joyce was going to come dowse the house.

"Do you know what dowsing is?" I asked her.

"No," she said.

"Why would it be an encouraging idea for you then?"

"I trust Joyce, that's all," Linda said with finality.

Joyce didn't waste any time. She came right away and from the pocket of her jeans withdrew some buttons on a short string, which she began to twirl. She moved quickly through the living and dining room, changing directions and holding the string which twirled continuously. She zipped through the kitchen and bathroom and ended up in our bedroom.

"There are no molds or fungus or dust that would be a problem here for me," she said. I felt a brief wave of exultation knowing that the carpet could stay, that we could stay. I loved my little house.

"There's some kind of radiation, though, here in the bedroom. It's coming from deep underground." She described a line with her hand that marked the place where Linda slept.

"I couldn't sleep in here," she said.

Linda was backing out of the room.

"What is it?" I asked. I was, with great difficulty, trying to comprehend how some kind of ray could be beaming up through the earth under our bed.

"It's like electromagnetic energy coming up from some fault line or mineral deposit under the surface of the earth. It's not from the basement. It's deeper. It's not good energy."

"Is the energy what's making me sick?" Linda asked in a stage whisper.

Joyce explained that it might not make her sick but could certainly keep her from getting well by putting stress on the immune system. She recommended Linda not sleep in that room.

"What can we do?" I wanted to know. "Is there anything we can do?"

"There's a man in Medford who can neutralize it. He can also do a much more thorough check of the house than I can. I'll call you with his number. His name is Mechem."

Linda gave Joyce a big hug. Joyce left and Linda dragged her blankets and quilts into the living room and made camp on the futon.

"Call that Mr. Mechem," she pleaded.

I was more than a bit skeptical that one could spin some buttons and determine that magnetic rays were shooting up through our bedroom floor. On the other hand, I had a strong sense that Joyce knew what she was talking about. I called Mechem and got an answering machine. The voice of an older man. Crisp. Professional. The next day I called it again and left another message. I couldn't reach Mr. Mechem.

I talked to Joyce to see if there was anyone else in the area who might be able to help. She suggested I hold out for Mr. Mechem.

"Mechem," she said, "is one person who can do the job for sure."

"How do you know about him?" I wanted to know.

"I heard him speak at the Dowsers Society meeting."

"You mean there's a bunch of you! Enough to have a meeting?"

"You'd probably be surprised," said Joyce. "While you're waiting for Mr. Mechem you might want to get Linda started on some SOD/CAT. Do you know what that is?"

"Of course I don't," I replied. "I'm starting to think I don't know anything. Tell me about it."

Joyce, who had a degree in molecular biology, gave me a brief lecture on free radicals. She asked me if I'd noticed all the TV commercials touting antioxidants. I had. She asked me to visualize a cell in the body which was absorbing oxygen and food to create energy. As part of the waste in this transaction, atoms with unpaired electrons are created. These are the "free radicals." In normal circumstances our body produces enough enzymes to convert the free radicals to harmless waste. But if there is a shortage of these enzymes, the free radicals can damage cells. The damage of cells leads to aging and possibly chronic disease. Stress is a condition which can cause free radicals to gain an upper hand over a healthy body's normal support systems. This stress can be caused by poor eating habits, drinking and smoking, pollution or pesticides in food, and by a myriad of force fields generated by computers, cosmic radiation, microwaves, power lines, and geopathic stress.

"What is geopathic stress?" I asked. I'd never heard that term before.

"It's what you've got in your bedroom," Joyce replied.

"Elimination of the stress is a key to the solution," she continued. "That's why you need Mechem. But that's only going to take care of those problems in and around the house. You can help support the body's own defenses by taking an antioxidant enzyme."

"Keep talking," I said. "I'm taking notes."

"Unhealthy oxygen atoms have an unpaired electron. They're the most common free radical. Our body produces an enzyme called superoxide dismutase or SOD. I won't explain why you also need catalase but you do."

"So what do we take?" I asked her.

"Try and find a product called Cell Guard. It was really helpful when I had arthritis," she said. "It's made of wheatgrass sprouts," she said.

"Wheatgrass! You're kidding," I shouted. "The wheatgrass people said you had to eat it raw. What's going on?"

"Well," said Joyce. "The SOD/CAT folks say you couldn't eat enough raw sprouts in a day to enhance the antioxidant enzyme levels the body needs. Each Cell Guard tablet has about a quart of sprouts, and you take six tablets a day."

"Wait till I tell Linda she's going to be eating six quarts of sprouts a day."

Mr. Mechem finally called me back. He didn't sound like the man on the phone message. His voice was raspy.

"Doctor says I have strep throat," he told me. "Sorry I took so long to call back."

"When can you come out?" I wanted to know.

"It'll be a while," he said. "The doctor gave me some pills. Told me to stay in bed. But we can get started. Draw me a floor plan of your house. Put in the main walls and identify the rooms like bedroom, kitchen, bathroom."

"Does it have to be scale?" I asked.

"No," said Mr. Mechem. "Just do your best. Try to show me where north is."

"What do you do with the diagram?" I wanted to know.

"I'll map dowse it and call you back," he replied.

I called Joyce. "He said he was going to map dowse it," I told her. "What's that?"

"It's sort of like telepathy," she answered.

It was quite a distance from Dr. Bond's office in Everett, Washington, to the land of telepathy, where an elderly gentleman holding a pendulum over a floor plan of our house could deduce malevolent forces radiating from beneath the surface of the earth below the foundation of our small structure.

Sometime during that period, our front door began to rattle suddenly one night in evidence of an earthquake centered east of us, which caused severe damage to the brick buildings of Klamath Falls, a city only fifty miles away. The earthquakes and aftershocks gave my mind a tilt which opened it wider to the concept of dowsing and geopathic disturbance. I would wait and see what Mechem had to say.

In the meantime, I drove to Wal-Mart to restock our supply of hydrogen peroxide and Epsom salts. Linda had become addicted to daily hot baths and her favorite mix was four pints of H_2O_2 and a quart of Epsom salts. She believed they were pulling toxins from her body. Some days she took two baths—one in the late morning to wake her up and soothe the pain; one at night to relax her aching muscles so she could go to sleep. At Safeway, Epsom salts was about $2.50 per half-gallon, and hydrogen peroxide was sixty-seven cents a pint. Since I had become accustomed to recording the costs of our adventures, I was able to quickly compute the cost of a single bath at $5.18. Two baths got us into some serious money. Water wasn't cheap in Ashland either, as the area was in the midst of a ten-year drought. When the big new Wal-Mart store opened a few miles out of town I was pleased, not only to be greeted by a smiling old man, who welcomed me to the store, but to discover that H_2O_2 sold routinely for seventeen cents per pint, with Epsom salts at $1.76. With Wal-Mart as a new partner, Linda's special baths now cost only $2.44. Two Wal-Mart baths were cheaper than one Safeway bath!

On my first visit I talked a Wal-Mart clerk into hauling five cases of hydrogen peroxide out of the stockroom. Subsequently, I had to buy it by the bottle and would invariably be asked by the checker what I was doing with all the hydrogen peroxide. This gave me the opportunity to give a short speech, to the checker and anyone behind me in line, on the therapeutic benefit of an H_2O_2/Epsom salts bath. It occurred to me as I looked around Wal-Mart that many of its shoppers could use therapy of some kind. On my occasional visits to Safeway, Bi-Mart and Albertson's, I began to pay attention to the shoppers and, more interestingly, to what the shoppers ate. I noted baskets full of fats and junk, desperately low on whole grains, fruits, and vegetables. I observed that the beverage section was one of the largest in every supermarket, and most shopping baskets seemed to contain a six-pack or two. Granted, Linda had managed to become ill on a wholesome diet, but I remained convinced she was sick in spite of the diet not because of it. I had the urge to stand near the checkout line and give speeches on right living to the overweight, pasty-skinned shoppers with their sugar-laden baskets. However, it seemed proper that I should get my own house in order before trying to save America from its eating habits. So I toted the hydrogen peroxide home and scoured and filled the tub one more time. Drawing a bath and lowering Linda into the tub was a consistent daily ritual.

Cleaning house was a frequent ritual also. I was a good house cleaner and had been since my days at Officer Training School (OTS) at Lackland Air Force Base. I had gone through OTS with an obsessive fear of failure. I was certain of one thing. I did not want to wash out and fail to get my commission as a Second Lieutenant. If one received too many gigs (demerits), he or she would be booted out of the program. Thus, I awoke each morning at 4.00 A.M. and used the palms of my hands to sweep every particle of dust from the linoleum floor, and my finger tips to clean the window sills and ledges of my drawers. The natural oil on hands and fingers helped pull the dust, preparing all surfaces for the daily white glove inspection conducted by evil little Captain Kafer. Kafer soon learned there were no woollies (dust balls) to be found under my bed and he quit bending down to look, allowing me the opportunity to break the rules and use paper clips and rubber bands to pull my sheet and blanket together so tightly that Captain Kafer's quarter would actually rebound slightly when he dropped it on my cot.

I had long passed the point where I was willing to use the palms of my hands as floor cleaning tools. I used broom, vacuum and, of course, drew from my large cache of hydrogen peroxide. Linda had an aversion to spending money on appliances. She would prefer to add another quilt to her collection. But now that she was nearly comatose, I decided to upgrade. We had gone through a series of bottom-of-the-line vacuum cleaners which seemed only to move the dirt around. I wanted to get something high-powered—a Kirby perhaps, or a Rainbow.

I started calling vacuum cleaner shops to get their advice. Because we had carpeting throughout the house, each salesman I spoke to recommended that I get a power head which would remove that deep-down hidden dirt. The consensus of opinion was that I needed a Princess. The thought of having a Princess appealed to me immediately. I called around again to recheck prices. Amazingly, Green's of Medford was $100 cheaper than any other store.

The next day, after making Linda a bowl of cream of rye with raisins, apples and bananas, I drove to Medford and Green's to check out the Princess. Green's sold sewing machines on one side and vacuum cleaners on the other. The vacuum cleaners were lined up in tight formation around the perimeter of the room and in a double rank down the center. The two salesmen were busy on the sewing machine side. I was wearing my dirty work pants, old tennis shoes, and a baseball cap; I needed a shave. A semi-attractive woman who had driven up just before me in a new BMW was waiting to be helped and was unenthusiastically touching the red handle of an upright called a Red Devil or maybe Dirt Devil. The salesman appeared.

"I'm first," said the woman, holding up her left hand as if to display her large diamond ring and gold watch. "I need a vacuum cleaner, and I believe this is the one my cleaning lady wanted me to buy," she said pointing to the red thing.

"What kind of features are you looking for?" the salesman wanted to know.

"Well, I don't want anything too expensive," she continued. "I'm sure this is the one my cleaning lady told me to purchase."

"Cleaning lady," I thought to myself. "That's what I am, a cleaning lady!" I kind of snorted causing the woman who had a cleaning lady to turn around and give me a dirty look.

"Do you want to try it out?" asked the salesman.

The woman pushed it a couple of times and said, "How much?"

"One hundred and eighty dollars," answered the salesman.

"This is the one my cleaning lady wanted, I'm sure," said the woman, mentioning her cleaning lady for the third time.

The salesman led her to the cashier and I was left alone. I looked for the Princess but couldn't find her among the Eurekas, Royals, and Dirt Devils.

"How can I help you?" asked the salesman who had sneaked up behind me.

"Show me a Princess," I said. "And keep in mind, it's not for my cleaning lady; it's for me."

He pulled a Princess out of the back room and hooked it up. The gray and chrome canister had a high-tech industrial look. It rolled on large castors which would allow the machine to move smoothly in any direction. Around the bottom of the canister was a soft vinyl cushion bumper which protected walls and furniture from collision damage. The canister would hold and trap two-and-a-half gallons of dust and dirt. There was no bag!

"No bag!" I cried happily, as the salesman showed me how the hemp filter would remove from the returning air stream dirt and dust particles as small as .3 microns in diameter.

"A micron is a millionth part of a meter," he said.

"I know that!" I lied enthusiastically.

"Bag-type vacuum cleaners are inefficient," he continued. "They often just stir up dust. Now, the Princess here is a cleaning system, not just a vacuum cleaner, and will help filter the air in the room as you clean. Look," he continued. "You can take this lid off and put a few drops of eucalyptus or some other essential oil on this felt pad, and the Princess will fill your home with cleansing aromas. And this hose. It is twelve feet long—way longer than most vacuum cleaner hoses. You could drive a car over the hose; it's so strong," he said twisting the hose into a ribbon. "See, it's tough. And, you're going to love the power head. It's one of the most powerful nozzles on the market. It's got its own motor which drives a revolving brush. What this does is separate the rug fibers and loosens deep imbedded dirt."

"I hate imbedded dirt," I told him.

"This baby will get it," he continued. "You've got your four-position setting on the power head. And, of course, you get a crevice tool, a brush, a floor brush, and a convertible six-inch brush—you know, the regular stuff. And," he continued dramatically, "bring her in once a year and we'll service her for free."

"The main thing I'm interested in," I told him, "is suction."

He smiled and walked over to the counter and picked up a gadget which turned out to be some kind of a gauge.

"This is my suckometer," he told me. "First I'm gonna show you a top-of-the-line Eureka. It costs $200 more than your Princess, here," he said in a whisper. He plugged in the Eureka which roared to life like an airplane engine. I was concerned. The Eureka sounded powerful.

He slid the meter onto the end of the Eureka's wand and held it up so I could see. The needle leapt to 80.

"Not bad," he said, flipping off the switch. He plugged in the Princess which had a kind of hum rather than the powerful roar of the Eureka. I was concerned. She didn't sound like she could hold her own with the big guys. I wanted her so badly, but performance was the key.

He placed the meter on the metal wand of the Princess and I briefly closed my eyes. When I opened them I broke into a wide grin. The needle was on 100. The salesman was grinning too.

"This little baby can really suck," he said. "You want her, don't you?"

"Of course, I do," I said in a firm voice, feeling sorry for the cleaning lady with her Dirt Devil.

During the month of November Linda stayed in bed. She was weak and had difficulty breathing. In the mornings she would cough up stuff, sounding like an old man, gagging on her expectorations. She remained positive that it was only a function of time until the effect of the ozone would manifest.

I vacuumed with great regularity using all my attachments, and pulled several gallons of dust, cat hair, dust mites, and their fecal matter from rugs, floors, upholstery, and bed. I experimented with eucalyptus, rosemary, and lavender and read the claims of the aromatherapy people of the therapeutic and healing effects of essential oils. I washed the windows, using a great tip from Martha Stewart. Electric dish-washing soap in hot water did leave my windows sparkling and streakless. A spray bottle of hydrogen peroxide was ready on the kitchen counter to foam away bacteria which lurked in the crevices around the faucets and the sink. The ozone generator was turned to "high" while I scrubbed the kitchen and bathroom floors with Pinesol. While I cleaned, I hoped for an idea which would lead us to a solution.

On her worst days Linda believed that she was dying. In the afternoon she would stand in front of the sink and slowly brush her hair. Then, after wiping up the hair ball in the sink with a wad of toilet paper, she would sigh and crawl back into bed. "I'll be completely bald by Christmas," she would say without emotion. "Bald and probably dead. Dead and bald."

"You're not going bald and you're not dying either," I'd reply firmly. But, I didn't know what to do. We had no plan.

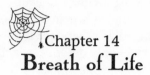

Chapter 14
Breath of Life

In late November I went to an all-day Tai Chi workshop. Several instructors, including Fred, gave demonstrations. Fred did the first two parts of Qigong; the others showed various forms of Tai Chi. A young woman performed a Tai Chi that was completely unlike the others. It was slow and dreamy and flowed like a dance. The movements were extremely soft. What impressed me was her breathing. Breathing was her dominant movement. You could hear and palpably feel each inhalation and each exhalation. When she exhaled she made a sighing sound which impressed me as both sensual and mechanical. She seemed to completely clear not only her lungs with each release of breath but her entire body. I was enthralled.

In the afternoon each instructor led those of us who were still there in some Tai Chi exercises, like push hands and balancing. But Micheline Burchard (that was her name) began to teach us how to breathe—to release and accept energy. She made us growl and stomp our feet and pull our hair and make grinding motions with our face. The experience was powerful and energizing. Following the workshop I approached her and asked, "Do you make housecalls? My wife is very ill and has been for a long time. She has difficulty breathing."

Micheline did everything in a relaxed, almost languorous manner. I waited minutes for her to speak, and during those minutes she fixed her gaze on mine until I felt like a cat who turns away when you stare at it. Micheline was an expert at intense eye contact, and as I got to know her better I came to believe that she thought she could communicate with those eyes. For reasons I am unable to explain, I can only take eye contact in small doses. Prolonged exposure to the gaze of another human gives me something akin to vertigo, leaving me feeling limp.

On a trip to Hawaii several years earlier, Dr. Bart had insisted I go Sufi dancing. I didn't know what Sufi dancing was then, nor do I now, but that evening's entertainment consisted of a number of men and women, many of whom were followers of Bhagwan Shri Rashnish, circling each other face-to-face and administering eye contact—which I could only describe as extremely painful. I am certain I could stare at someone's most private parts longer than I can their eyes; and I only survived the Sufi dance by using all my will power. When someone stares at me for longer than five seconds, I begin to fear they may be insane; or worse, that they might drive me over the brink.

Perhaps Micheline could communicate with her eyes, but more horrifying to me was the thought that she might be able to see in my eyes things I wanted no one else to see.

"Do you think you could?" I asked, then coughed and cleared my throat and pulled out a handkerchief and removed my glasses and wiped them off and rubbed my eyes, inventing every diversion I could muster to avoid staring back at those blinkless pools of energy.

"It. . .it could. . .could be very interesting," she said. "I've never. . .I've never taught one-on-one. It could be interesting."

"Will you?" I asked, scratching my forehead and the back of my neck and looking at my watch.

"I'll think about it," said Micheline, staring at my eyes as if she were searching for my true motivation.

"You can call me," she said. "It could be interesting."

It was around the 1st of December. There was snow in the mountains. Each morning when I went outside and practiced Qigong in our backyard, the top of Grizzly Peak would be dusted with fresh snow. Curiously, I enjoyed the cold air and was certain that my tolerance to cold had increased. I noticed that on afternoon hikes a wool shirt was enough to keep me comfortable. It was not so much a tolerance of cold; it was more akin to enjoyment. This I attributed to Qigong. While I was outside flapping my arms, breathing, and stretching into strange bird-like postures, Linda huddled under quilts near her beloved gas stove, thinking about warmer climates.

It was on such a day that "Mich" (Micheline) decided to come. I was surprised when she showed up, for I had heard the snow was a foot deep up in the mountainous Greensprings area where she lived, and when she arrived there was snow on the top of her four-wheel drive Subaru station wagon, evidence of an accurate weather report.

Had it not been for her eyes, I would not have recognized her. At the Tai Chi workshop she had been dressed plainly with her hair pulled back. This day, she was dressed for town, with dress and leather boots and thick hair to her shoulders. She came in silently, communicating with her eyes, removing her coat. I tried small talk. She smiled. I introduced her to Linda who had wobbled in from the bedroom.

"I guess I'll leave you two alone," I said, "to breathe! Heh, heh."

They seemed to instantly form a rapport, and now four eyes drilled me like I was extra baggage. I backed out of the house and walked, pleased to be relieved, for an hour at least, as caretaker.

When I returned Linda was glowing. She seemed more relaxed than she had been in a month.

"How was it?" "What did you do?" I asked her, taking a seat on the edge of the bed.

"She's teaching me to breathe. To really breathe. She's showing me how to release my breath."

"Did she talk?" I wondered.

"Oh yes. She talked a lot. She has such vitality—and those eyes! She's coming back next week again. I think she can really help me."

It was very encouraging to see Linda pulled out of her winter depression. I had learned during this long illness that she did better mentally if she was working with someone.

I drove to the food store to get some groceries. The first person I saw when I entered the store was Mich. Impetuously, I gave her a big hug. It was a big hug, but a short hug. Mich seemed flustered by my attack, which confused me because I had observed her at the Tai Chi workshop share about a five-minute hug with some friend. She stared at me.

"Thanks for spending the time with Linda," I stammered, while trying to comprehend from her expression if I had made a hugging mistake or violated some hugging protocol. Hugging is not one of my specialties. I am not good at it. Invariably, when hugging is taking place, I am standing in the wrong position or facing the wrong direction. I have never learned to flow properly into a hug, and thus make every effort to avoid them. If I do get into a hugging position, I can't figure out what to do with my arms. Do I go low with both arms? High with both arms? Or, do I attempt a right arm high, left arm low maneuver. Being tall makes hugging additionally awkward. Short women end up buried in my chest; tall ones, after a clumsy clanking of arms, end up cheek-to-cheek as if at a high school dance. I have studied huggers, primarily Linda, who can gracefully move into and out of multiple embraces, while I stand by like Forrest Gump with my mouth open, trying to get a bead on who I might hug and how I might do it.

Thus, standing in the food store with Micheline staring at me with her most expressive eyes, my brain raced, searching my hugging files, trying to figure out if I had screwed up. I decided I had simply caught her by surprise, next to the herbal remedies.

"I like Linda," she said after a long pause. "I'm coming again next week."

"She told me a bit about what you did. What exactly is it that you're doing? What kind of work is it? It's not Tai Chi."

With Mich I found myself unable to stand the silence and tried to fill the space between our eyes with words.

"Reich," she said.

"What?"

"Wilhelm Reich. I trained with a student of Reich's work."

"Tai Chi?"

"I had a Tai Chi teacher, too," she told me.

"Wilhelm Reich was a Tai Chi teacher?" I babbled.

"No, no. . .My first teacher was a student of Wilhelm Reich's work. Then I studied with a Tai Chi teacher."

"Wasn't Reich the guy who invented the orgone box?" I asked.

Micheline smiled and kind of giggled. "I'll come by and see Linda next week."

I unloaded groceries and carefully folded the bags and walked the mile and a half to the Southern Oregon State College Library to check out Wilhelm Reich. After a few hours of skimming several books by and about him, I was shocked that his life had not been made into a major motion picture. Vilified as a mad, sex-crazed scientist by some and nearly deified as a father of new age thought by others, Reich, from either viewpoint, was a fascinating and provocative character. An Austrian Jew, a student and protégé of Freud, he had become disenchanted with Freud's techniques of analysis and had developed his own methods of therapy. Moving away from Freud, Reich gained a few followers and many enemies.

Where Freud focused on dreams and childhood memory, Reich focused on the body. He studied his patient's body language, facial expression, vocal quality, method of breathing, and rigidities. These rigidities he labeled "body armor," and he theorized that this armor was the result of conflicts which build up gradually in layers. Reich believed that armoring resulted from our life experiences beginning in the womb. If the mother was overly emotional, used drugs, alcohol, or tobacco, this would create conflicts for the fetus. Childbirth, or what Reich described as the sterile experience of unnatural childbirth, was a second source of armoring. Lack of breast feeding was another. The process continued in the restricted environment of classrooms, with life in unaffectionate families and the competitiveness of playground and workplace.

His therapy was to dissolve the body armor which resulted in release of old emotions and, concurrently, in streamings of energy. Reich felt that body armor blocked the free flow of biologic energy throughout the body. These blocks were in seven areas: around the eyes, around the mouth and jaws, in the neck/throat/shoulders, in the upper chest, in the diaphragm, in the abdominal area which included the lower back, and rectum and in the pelvis, which included the legs.

Reich would have patients strip to underwear and socks, as does a massage therapist, and lie on a couch. He sat beside them in a chair, unlike the Freudians who would sit behind the patient, out of their field of vision. Therapy with Reich could last several months to a year but was a much shorter program than that of the Freudians. Therapy started at the top of the body and worked down. Breathing was very important, and as Reich pressed on various points in the armor, he would insist that his patients breathe deeply and rhythmically.

In a successful dissolution of body armor the patient would sense streamings of energy and flexibility of emotion. This would happen during the therapy session. Subsequently, a patient progressing in their therapy, would, while making love, experience what Reich called orgiastic release, "the capacity to surrender to the flow of biological energy, without any inhibition, the capacity for complete discharge of all dammed-up sexual excitation through involuntary pleasurable contractions of the body." (Therapy would lead to orgiastic release in one's person life; not during the therapy session).

His focus on orgasm as evidence of the emotional well-being of individuals was a precursor of things to come. It was also fuel for slander by his enemies and critics.

The object of Reich's therapy was to promote "vegetative aliveness" in the entire organism. This aliveness was characterized by muscular release which initiated energy streamings. Release of body armor produced by freer breathing and the skill of the therapist would, over time, result in feelings of warmth, prickling in the skin, and muscular shuddering which would finally produce a convulsive reflex movement wherein the entire body appeared to be expanding and contracting. Breathing was seen as a primary regulator of energy, of aliveness. If one could breathe freely, one would feel more alive and able to cope.

Clearly, Reich saw a mind-body connection, and he was critical of mainstream medicine for departmentalizing the two parts of the human entity and for generally discounting emotions as causative factors in wellness or illness. The degenerative diseases of the twentieth century—heart disease, cancer, etc.—were caused, according to Reich, by a malfunction or blockage of the body's biological energies. Infectious diseases like colds, flu, or even typhoid and tuberculosis were also affected by a person's emotional state. What else could explain why, when many people were exposed to a disease, not all would succumb to it.

Later in his career Reich became convinced that a subtle energy akin to electricity, magnetism, or radiation permeates all living things. He called this orgone. Orgone, like ch'i, produces an energy field around all living things. Orgone was, according to Reich, freely available in the atmosphere and could be collected in a specially-built contraption called an orgone accumulator. The orgone accumulator was just big enough for a person to sit in, and Reich rented these boxes to physicians for the low fee of $10 per month, so they could experiment to see if increasing the supply of orgone to ill patients could assist in healing. Many positive results were reported.

It is an involved story, worthwhile to explore, about Reich's run-ins with the medical establishment and the Food and Drug Administration. Reich died in humiliation in a federal prison, found guilty of violating an injunction not to ship the orgone accumulators (black boxes). His books were banned and actually burned, but in the 1960s and 1970s his ideas were revived by a number of therapists and practitioners.

I had no idea if Mich was a certified practitioner. Experience of the last year had told me that certificates meant less than results. Linda was still quite ill, but her sessions with Mich were, at the very least, breathing new life into her attitude. As Linda described the sessions to me, they seemed to follow the pattern of top to bottom I had read about in the books on Reich. Mich spent most of her time leading Linda through breathing exercises and focusing on her eyes and jaw. Linda was getting good at the sensual exhalation of air from her lungs. I wanted to know if there had been any discussion of orgiastic potency. I was a bit nervous about where this therapy might lead. But Micheline had not used that terminology. She had suggested, however, that Linda visualize relaxing her pelvic muscles completely and exhaling through her vagina. Since this was kind of a scary idea to me, I put some distance between myself and these sessions, hoping only that they would help Linda through the winter months, trusting that spring would bring new solutions, and that vitamins and antioxidant enzymes would begin to effect a cure and give her body strength to heal itself.

After the third session I returned to the house too soon. Mich wanted to talk to me privately. Linda was still in the bedroom. I suggested the breakfast nook. We sat opposite each other, Mich staring at me but not speaking. Fighting the desire to wiggle, I attempted to stare back. She had wanted to talk but wasn't saying anything. She seemed so comfortable and relaxed just sitting there. She was confident, even powerful. I decided that she just knew things I didn't know. Nonverbal communication techniques might be one of these things. Finally, not being able to stand the silence, I asked her what she wanted to tell me. It seemed to take her forever to say a very few words. I felt she was talking in a code. I wasn't sure I'd understand. I was too stupid for her. Too slow. The gist was that she thought I should consider joining one of her classes. Because of the techniques she was teaching, Mich worried that Linda might "get way ahead of me." She looked at me even more closely, as if trying to discern if I understood what she was telling me. The strange thing was that I did understand. Granted, without my research on Dr. Wilhelm Reich, I might have been in the dark. I responded by agreeing to come to a class.

"You should wear loose clothing," she told me, "so you can breathe easier."

After she left, I breathed easier. Nevertheless, I looked forward to the class, not wanting to be left behind.

In mid-December I got hold of Mr. Mechem. He was still ill with strep throat. He had, however, taken the time to map dowse our house.

"There are some problems we need to take care of," he told me. "There's a sixty-cycle harmonic in the kitchen, probably coming from your circuit breakers. Do you have a computer?" he asked.

I told him I did and that it was set up in the breakfast nook.

"I'm surprised it works," he told me.

"It works okay," I said. "What about the bedroom?"

"You've got a real problem in the bedroom with geopathic stress," he said. "There's an underground water stream that intersects with a magnetic grid line right about at the head of your bed. The radiation from either one is harmful but when they intersect that way it's really a problem. It's no wonder your wife is having trouble getting well."

This was essentially the same thing Joyce had told us.

"What can we do?" I wanted to know.

"We can neutralize it," said Mechem. "But I've got to come out and check it. Then we'll place some magnets around and pound some iron bars in the ground. That will neutralize it. Then you won't have anything to worry about."

"How much do you charge for this?" I asked him.

"Fifty dollars," he told me.

"Well, when can you get here?"

"Doctor tells me to stay home until I kick this bug. I probably won't be able to get down there until after Christmas."

Linda was disappointed at this news but there was nothing we could do but wait for Mechem. He told me he was one of the few people in the country who could neutralize geopathic stress in houses. I guessed we were lucky that we'd learned about him, identified the problem, and were going to eventually see him. Linda continued to sleep in the living room.

My brother Bart called that week. He was excited because he had an appointment to see a man who could diagnose illness with a machine.

"Are you sick?" I asked him.

"My head aches all the time," he told me.

Bart had heard about the machine from a friend. The diagnosis cost $500. Included in that price were any homeopathic remedies that might be prescribed. Bart explained that probes were placed on your fingers and toes and somehow this would tell what was ailing you. It sounded farfetched to me. Bart told us the man would be in the Seattle area for Christmas and Linda could see him then.

"I don't know," I told him. "We're planning to stay here for Christmas."

"Better think about it," said Bart. "I'll call you after my appointment and give you more details."

I drove down to Ashland's Railroad District and parked in front of the Bundini Building. It didn't appear anyone was there. But Mich's Subaru was parked in front so I went on in. I was wearing sweat pants and sweatshirt. There was a small anteroom next to the large polished hardwood floor of the studio. In the anteroom was a couch. Mich was on the couch talking to a man and woman she seemed to know quite well. I took off my jacket and sat on a bench opposite them. Quite casually she introduced me to "my classmates," and they continued their quiet discussion.

I sat on the bench, not listening, realizing that I was apprehensive. It was difficult for me to decide if the anxiety was about the class or just being in a new group. I decided it was the class. Perhaps it was Micheline. Her energy was overwhelming. The conventional view of a high-energy person is normally framed by their performance in group situations. They are often outgoing, sometimes loud, frequently dominating, usually talkative and even, rarely, intimidating. Micheline, the instructor, was none of the above. She stayed in her own space, talked quietly and very little, or not at all, and led by example. As she motioned for our small group to form a circle, she had the attention and respect of all the members of the group. I removed my shoes and joined the circle.

To this date, by actual count, during the course of her illness, Linda had had 136 appointments with doctors, dentists, massage therapists, acupuncturists, medical labs, and other therapists. This would be my first experience during that time frame with one of her therapies. Although this was advertised as a Tai Chi class, most of the time was spent on breathing exercises.

We stood in a circle, knees bent, arms relaxed, and breathed deeply, following Mich's example, making a noise with the exhalation. We were instructed to fill our lungs completely—right up to the clavicles. Relaxing my stomach, as Mich instructed, I discovered it was easier to draw in a complete breath of air. After four or five deep breaths I felt slightly dizzy. Along with the lightheadedness was a feeling that I was using unused muscles. I wondered if I'd ever breathed properly. Linda pointed out to me frequently that I held my breath, especially while asleep. (Reich said that to hold one's breath for a long time meant a heroic feat of self-control). I knew this was called sleep apnea, though I had none of the daytime symptoms which make it a serious ailment for many people. Perhaps the popularity of aerobic exercise comes from the requirement to breathe freely and deeply. Because of polluted air or the stale recirculated air of offices, we discourage ourselves from breathing deeply and evenly. Personally, I have always found the sound of a deep breather, especially a nose breather, somewhat offensive in a small group situation and have made an effort, however misguided, to learn to breathe quietly so as not to offend.

In this small circle of heavy breathers, noise was the thing, and it relaxed inhibitions while providing a noticeable rush. We breathed and pulled our hair and stamped our feet and growled as we pushed air out of our lungs, vividly demonstrating, even to a novice breather, the therapeutic value of something as basic as taking a deep breath of oxygen and releasing it completely.

Reich, with his emphasis on breathing, had discovered a truth which the Chinese had known for thousands of years—that is, breathing increases one's vital energy. In addition, the physical act of breathing deeply massages and stimulates the organs of the abdominal cavity. This is, in essence, the basis for medical Qigong.

Micheline invited the class to do the Tai Chi form. The group lined up in a loose formation. Mich stood at the head of the group with her back to us. I had recently taken a few Tai Chi classes from Fred Epping and had, in addition, taught myself a few movements from an illustrated book on Tai Chi. This group knew the entire form, so I expected to be completely lost. Once again, however, the emphasis seemed to be on breathing. I was twenty feet away from Mich, yet could hear each pull and push of her breath. The form seemed unimportant. It was only to set a rhythm for breathing. The movements were a dance, a percussion beat for the melody of air. The form was so slow I could, by staying a half-beat behind, find my way. As we turned and I got a look at the others, I realized they were all doing it a bit differently anyway. In Fred's class, he was quick to note and correct errors in form. He told us we should be able to tell two students of the same teacher. They would re-create the form as taught. In this class, we breathed our way through the Tai Chi, then sat in chairs to continue the breathing exercise and, unfortunately for me, make heavy eye contact.

We were to breathe and try to exchange energy with our eyes. My defense shields flew up, firmly in place, and in a state of disconcertment, I struggled through the end of the class, fearing I might faint when paired off with the oracular power of Micheline. I made it through three more classes before the holidays, and I was becoming only slightly more comfortable.

Linda was breathing better but she was still sick and weak. The cold weather was hard on her. She had all the old aches and pains and fears. We had spent a year and a half and thousands of dollars trying everything we could. I had read at least thirty books on a variety of subjects including nutrition, herbalism, homeopathy, aromatherapy, arthritis, Qigong, naturopathy, candida, oxygen, etc., and though now educated in many heretofore unexplained areas of alternative therapy, we were seemingly no closer to a "cure" than we had been when we started.

A week before Christmas Bart called again. He was very excited. He had seen the man with the machine and insisted we make an appointment. He was certain, he told me, that a Douglas Leber, assisted by what he described as an electroacupuncture machine, could diagnose and prescribe remedies which would put Linda back on the road to good health. What else could we do? Bart had been our scout throughout the entire experience. He had always been our ace in the hole, our entree to the hidden worlds. Perhaps Douglas Leber could help. Besides, Linda needed the motivation for hoping. We had about run out of practitioners to see. Mr. Leber was still in Hawaii. I called and talked to his wife. We could see him at his mother's home in the Seattle area two days after Christmas. Appointment #137 was noted on the calendar.

Chapter 15

Doug's Diagnosis

Here's all we knew about Douglas Leber before meeting with him at his mother's house two days after Christmas of 1993.

He received training as a naturopathic doctor in Seattle and was a licensed acupuncturist and colonic therapist. Since his graduation from naturopathic college he had specialized in investigational biomedical research using EAV (electroacupuncture according to Dr. Voll). Leber had developed an investigational tool called the Computron. The Computron was allegedly capable of completing a noninvasive assessment of all systems of the body. A client would hold metal electrodes, and the operator of the Computron would test all acupuncture meridians, organs, and systems of the body. With the Computron Doug Leber would:

1. Conduct a complete noninvasive physical exam and provide a printout of the results.

2. Identify the root cause of symptoms.

3. Test for toxic metals, chemical allergies, food allergies, parasites, and viruses.

4. Identify subhealth conditions before they manifested on standard medical tests.

5. Provide a course of action to restore the health of the body using homeopathics, herbs, vitamins, minerals, and dietary recommendations.

Using the Computron to gather information, he would then look for confirming evidence in the individual's medical history and symptoms in order to assess problem areas.

Our initial consultation, which was supposed to last approximately two and one-half hours, would cost $500. This would include any initial treatments and homeopathic remedies. According to our information from Dr. Bart, Douglas Leber was also working with a biochemist on special formulas for chronic degenerative diseases including candida and Epstein Barr virus. The cost of these remedies, if prescribed, would be extra.

This information, even though we decided to act on it, was confusing. The Computron, in the hands of Douglas Leber, purportedly could do everything we had been trying to do for the previous year and a half. It promised a diagnosis to the level of root causes and a course of treatment. How could it be that simple? Why didn't every doctor have a Computron in his or her office? I was nearly a full-fledged advocate of alternative medicine although, as yet, it had not worked for us. The Computon, though, exuded the stinky sniff of quackery.

I called Bart back to ask him how it worked. He told me he really didn't know. It had something to do with electrical differences in the body. He also told me that Douglas Leber had seen eighteen people in Hawaii that week, many of whom were friends and acquaintances. We had a control group.

"He travels all over the world," said Bart.

"Why don't people come to him?" I wondered.

"I don't know," Bart replied. "Just make sure you keep that appointment."

Noble and Kendra were traveling with us to my parent's house for Christmas. We kenneled the cats and loaded our Suburban, installing the third seat so Linda could use it as a bed. Kendra made a nest for her of quilts and pillows. We locked the house and headed north on Interstate 5. At rest stops we would laboriously remove Linda from the third seat, help squeeze moccasins onto her fat, swollen feet, and help her walk to the ladies room. She wore a skirt with an elastic waistband for easy access. Her fingers were so swollen and stiff she could not zip or button for herself. She could barely pull up and pull down.

When we arrived at my mom and dad's condo, Linda went straight to bed and, except for brief interludes, stayed there through Christmas, sleeping a lot, eating little, racked with pains. Each night, as had become our habit, she would wake me up once or twice to massage the particularly painful areas so she could sleep some more. Linda was gathering strength for her next adventure.

Our appointment was set for 1:00 P.M. on the 27th, and we left before noon to drive the forty miles or so to Douglas Leber's mother's house. He didn't live in Hawaii; his residence was somewhere in the southwest, and he was at his mother's for Christmas before returning home.

His directions were very clear, and we found the white farmhouse which sat with its outbuildings like an oasis surrounded by shopping centers. We arrived early. It was 12:30 P.M. and, at first, no one answered the back door, which was a screen door leading to a porch. From where I stood knocking I could see part of the kitchen, and at the end of the kitchen table sat a man holding onto a wire.

Finally, a sixtyish woman with neatly curled and colored hair came to the door and invited us in. I waved to Linda to follow but had to go back to the car, as the door was too heavy for her to open by herself. We followed the smiling gray-haired woman into her living room. Once again, instead of finding ourselves in a modern medical clinic, we were in someone's living room, looking for help.

The house was decorated for Christmas with a large tree and hundreds of dolls, which Doug's mother had collected from around the world. There were many large elf-like creatures standing near the fireplace and in corners and alcoves of the old house which added to the surreal aspect of this experience. Linda sat weakly on a couch and tried to make conversation with Doug's mother—a lively, energetic woman who did her best to keep us company while we waited. And as we were to end up waiting for two and a half hours, she was able to relate her interesting life story and details of many of her travels. It was difficult for me to concentrate on her tales. I was anxious to get Linda hooked up to the Computron and find out what it did. Doug's mother focused her energies on Linda, no doubt recognizing she needed a boost, and the two and a half hours passed relatively quickly while we waited for Doug to finish with his current client.

Finally, as 3:00 P.M. arrived we were ushered into the kitchen where the Computron was set up on the kitchen table. Douglas Leber then appeared, a very large man dressed in loose beige clothing, his head covered with longish curly black hair, his face wreathed by a bushy black beard. I couldn't guess his age. He was somewhere between thirty and forty. He was large, wide, substantial looking. His face, though obscured, was extremely kind and he radiated intelligence. He was not what I expected. Bart had provided no physical description. Linda took a seat in a kitchen chair, and I pulled one up beside her. I was lugging a gym bag full of vitamins and supplements, as Bart had told us Leber could check their efficacy on his machine.

Doug Leber invited us to give him some background while he made himself a sandwich. He had worked through the lunch hour. The kitchen counters were strewn with the residue of a Christmas feast, including the partially gnawed carcass of a turkey which had taken on the dull brown color of leftover meat. I was disappointed that our latest health practitioner was not a vegetarian but had learned that vegetarianism was not a tenant of naturopathy. I told our story as Doug scooped dressing and gravy into a sauce pan and sliced some meat from the turkey's breastbone for a sandwich. Thus, I had an adequate amount of time to relate our adventures while he ate. He chewed and nodded, asking few questions and when he finished, washed his hands, took a seat opposite Linda, and asked her to remove her shoes. A drop of gravy was stuck to his mustache on the left side of his mouth.

I pulled my chair around so I was sitting between them. They faced each other and I was looking directly at the Computron. It was a computer with a monitor. Douglas Leber handed Linda a piece of copper attached to a wire which led to the Computron. Another wire led to a metal plate which looked like a grill for pancakes. The plate had a well in the center. Doug held a third wire in his hand which had a metal probe on the end. He began his procedure with no introduction or explanation. We had found our way to his mother's kitchen; it was assumed that we knew why we were there.

On the monitor was an outline of a human hand and a bar graph which rose and fell as Doug touched the probe at different spots on Linda's fingers. The machine made a kind of whooping noise as the bars on the graph rose and dropped again. It was an eerie sound and, intuitively, Linda and I were able to differentiate between a "good" sound and a "bad" sound. Lots of bad sounds coming from the machine.

Doug worked quickly and silently, occasionally asking a question, frequently laying down his probe to enter data on his keyboard. If I asked a question, he would stop and answer it clearly and in detail. He was an excellent, patient teacher. He was totally into his work, oblivious to time. The pictures on the screen changed as he probed and typed, the Computron whooped and, at intervals, he gave us expositions on the skin as an organ of elimination, Hering's Law of cure, the problems of toxic burden on the liver, and the polarity of electrons in the blood.

The hours came and went. Doug probed. Linda sat silently. I stared at the monitor. At 3:00 P.M. we had started what was advertised as a two and one-half hour procedure. At 6:00 P.M. Doug's wife and mother slipped quietly into the kitchen, careful not to disturb his concentration, and removed covered dishes from the refrigerator and carried them back to the dining room. We continued with no breaks. As hunger swept over me, I quit asking questions in order to speed the process. Time was clearly of no concern to the inventor of the Computron. He would probe until the answers were revealed. He was in a healing zone.

Suddenly, I noted the words "geopathic stress" appear on the screen. This startled me.

"What's geopathic stress?" I asked. I had unintentionally omitted telling him about Joyce and Mr. Mechem when I had recounted our medical history to him.

Doug stopped and carefully answered the question. "There are often noxious emanations, radiations if you will, coming from the ground. These affect you most if they are located where you spend a lot of time—such as your bedroom. These radiations can come from a variety of sources. They won't always make you ill but if you are ill they can diminish the strength of your immune system and keep you from getting well. Linda has severe geopathic stress."

"I don't understand," I said, playing dumb and wanting to hear more. "There's something in our bedroom?"

"Probably," said Doug Leber.

"What is it?" I asked him. "Where is it?"

Doug put down the probe and handed me a small piece of paper and a pencil.

"Draw me a diagram of your bedroom," he ordered.

I quickly drew an outline of the bedroom showing the door, windows, and location of the bed. Doug picked up the diagram, laid it on the kitchen table, and placed his hand over it moving it back and forth.

"What are you doing?" I asked.

"I'm map dowsing," he told me.

Then he held his hand in front of Linda's chest, palm out, and moved it back and forth. Turning back to the diagram he picked up the pencil and drew some lines. He picked up the piece of paper and showed it to us.

"You've got an underground vein of water which runs sort of east and west through this end of the room," he told us, indicating a line that ran across the head of our bed. "This is intersected by a Hartman Grid line, a magnetic field, which goes north and south. As you can see it intersects at this point. Who sleeps there?"

"I do," said Linda.

"The lines intersect right where your head hits the pillow," said Doug. "An intersection of these noxious energies creates a hot spot which can be very harmful to health."

"What should we do?" I asked.

"You need to move the bed as soon as you get home. That will get you off the top of these energies. You could also get some crystals and line them against the wall, here and here," he said, indicating the points where the lines hit the wall.

I was in a mild state of shock. For the third time in a month someone, first Joyce, then Mechem, now Doug Leber, had told us we had geopathic energies emanating from beneath the earth located in our bedroom. Two of the three, Mechem and Leber, had arrived at these identical conclusions using only a crudely drawn "map" of the house—or in Doug's case, of the bedroom. Using only the power of their minds they were somehow able to tap into an information source which provided them details about geopathic rays located in our bedroom in Ashland, Oregon. Mechem was located fifteen miles away in Medford. But Doug Leber was sitting 500 miles away in Seattle. It had been amazing enough that Joyce could detect these things using her pendulum while in the room. Mechem, based on the fact that we had been referred to him by Joyce for a geopathic stress problem, could have made a guess that we had something going on in the bedroom. However, in Leber's case we had not even raised the question of geopathic stress. He had detected the problem using the Computron and then quickly map-dowsed our bedroom, and had come to the same conclusion as Mr. Mechem.

In that instant, I became a believer in dowsing and in Douglas Leber's abilities. This was my first corroborated proof of the powers of telepathy, ESP, psychic ability, or whatever one wishes to call it. I knew that when we left that kitchen, we would have answers and remedies. This guy was for real. I experienced a wave of exultation.

We had been at it for four hours. I was surprised that Linda was holding up, surprised she wasn't complaining of cold feet. The probing continued and now it appeared that he was checking for remedies. I could see lists of names on the screen, names like lobelia, and as Doug moved his cursor down the list the Computron whooped and beeped. Doug bent over and rummaged through his bag and finally found some capsules. He placed them in the well on the metal plate and probed some more. He had Linda hold the copper wire next to her jaw. I couldn't understand what was going on. I didn't want to ask.

He handed one of the capsules to her and poured her a glass of bottled water.

"Take this," he told her. Then he put another identical capsule in front of her.

"Take this one in ten minutes."

"What is it?" she asked. "What's it doing?" This was Linda's first question in four hours.

"Your blood is in left spin," he replied. "This is a type of amino acid. It will spin your blood the other direction and help enable your liver to deal with toxins."

"That's good," Linda said. She was sitting up straighter in her chair, looking brighter than she had in some days.

"I'm feeling better already," said Linda, smiling at me. She took the other capsule.

"Thank God for the placebo effect," I thought, too hungry to ask about left-spinning blood.

"Have you figured out what's wrong?" I finally asked at about 7.30 P.M.

"Just about," said Doug Leber. "Now I'm figuring out what remedies to give you. My printer isn't working," he continued. "If you want to take some notes, I'll tell you what we've got here."

Finally, after a year and a half, someone was going to tell us something. My hopes were high, my pencil was poised. Here's what Doug Leber told us:

"Linda has three areas of focal toxicity. A focus is an area where toxins have been stored by the body in an attempt to wall them off. This can take the form of infection or an abscess. The body can normally handle one focal infection without noticeable difficulty. It takes three to throw the body out of balance. Geopathic disturbance counts as an additional focus. So, in effect, you have four. You have an infection in your jaw (ostitis); there's an abscess in your liver caused by E. histolytica, which is an amoeba you get from drinking water; and there's a chronic hidden infection in your tear gland which could be caused by a combination of an ant bite and giardia—another amoeba. You've had this tear gland (or lachrymal) infection for many years but your immune system was probably able to keep it in check until all the other problems developed. Now as far as the foci are concerned, natural medicine can assist with reducing toxicity, but if they progress beyond a certain point, as in the case of your jaw, surgery is the indicated procedure."

I was writing feverishly. Linda sat staring at Doug, rapt with attention, eyes watery.

"I don't find any evidence of candidiasis or tapeworm, so perhaps your ozone therapy was helpful there. But with all these infections dripping toxins through your body, the immune system is overwhelmed, endocrine function becomes weak, digestion becomes inefficient, and as a result of all normal bodily functions and defenses getting out of balance, you continue in a downward spiral. Viruses that live in the body but which normally won't cause problems begin to gain ground. So, in your case, Linda, I'm finding hepatitis A, Epstein Barr, mumps, and a flu virus—Grippe V '90. In addition, you have some metal toxicity from methyl mercury, gold, and lead."

"What causes me to ache so much?" she asked, on the verge of sobs.

"A lot of it seems to be caused by the infection of the lachrymal, the tear gland. Also, all of these toxins can cause allergic reactions, so it's no surprise you've had such a variety of symptoms."

"What do we do?" I asked.

Doug Leber was bent over, rummaging through a large black doctor's satchel. It was very disorganized, and it was nearly five minutes before he found what he was looking for and spoke again.

"Our pretreatment is going to focus on the liver. You've already taken an amino acid which will get your blood out of its left spin. We need to clean up the blood so the liver can do its job."

"Can a liver really regenerate?" I asked him.

"It can if it isn't substantially damaged. In Linda's case the liver will heal. It will just take some time. Most important is to get cavitation surgery on the left upper second and third molars—numbers fifteen and sixteen."

"Where?" asked Linda.

"You need to see a dentist who is a member of the Academy of Biological Dentistry. I'll give you some names. You need to do this within six weeks."

"We need to give you some adrenal supplements and B vitamins to give you a boost."

At that moment activity seemed to pick up in the kitchen as Doug's mother and wife tiptoed past the kitchen table to return dirty dishes. In the days before fancy clinics, when healers made house calls, this was, I supposed, how it was done.

"Here is some B-6, pantothenic acid, and some adrenal formula," Doug continued. "I'm going to give you four doses of an amino acid. You'll take two within a ten-minute span every other day. I'm giving you an antihepatitis medicine which you take one each day for five days, then skip for five days, and then repeat one a day for five days. Also, I'm giving you some remedies which will knock out the Epstein Barr and flush out the toxic metals. Wait a couple of days to start these and take them at 4:00 in the afternoon. I'm also going to make you a bottle of Lugol's Iodine water."

He went to the porch and came back with a large bottle of Crystal Geyser water, removed the cap, and from a small plastic vial, put about two drops into the bottle. He shook it and labeled it.

"I want you to drink eight glasses of pure water every day. Crystal Geyser is the best. This is a very important factor in good health. Tap water has parasites. Good water has quality-controlled PH and oxidation/reduction sensitivity. . .the ions dissolve in water."

"We have a reverse osmosis system," I told him.

"That's good."

"The filters need changing," said Linda.

"Why don't you drink bottled water for awhile," he suggested. "Drink two ounces of Lugol's water a day. Measure it out; don't guess. This will get your thyroid going. Try and take a coffee enema once a week to help flush out your liver."

"And move the bed," said Linda.

"Move the bed," nodded Doug. "I don't have my printer so can't give you a printout today, but I will mail it to you. I'll also be sending five homeopathic remedies and two botanicals. Those are included in the fee. The capsules are extra."

I had my checkbook out. "How much should I make this for then?" I asked.

"Seven hundred dollars," replied Doug.

I wrote him a check while he wrote a receipt. He put the capsules in plastic zip-lock bags and labeled them. It was 9:30 P.M. We had been with him for five and a half hours! Doug had seen only two people that day. We had answers and remedies. We thanked him profusely. He acknowledged the thanks with modesty.

"Get that cavitation surgery as soon as possible," he told us, handing me a piece of paper with names and phone numbers. "Be patient," he said to Linda. "You'll have some ups and downs, but you will get well."

We left the kitchen and walked to the car, Linda holding tightly to her Lugol's Iodine bottle. In the car, Linda, of course, began to sob. We gave each other a high-five. This was our best adventure to date. We had the diagnosis we'd searched for so long. I was certain she would get well. Linda was clearly revived, and when we arrived at my mom's kitchen an hour later, Linda ate three pieces of homemade pizza. She ate it with much gusto, smiling all the while.

Chapter 16
Understanding Energy

The holidays passed quickly. Linda was up more, moving around and seemingly enjoying herself. Even though there was no great diminution of symptoms, she just felt better. Deepak Chopra, the ubiquitous guru of alternative medicine says, "If you are feeling better, you are getting better." I was in somewhat of a daze. For well over a year we had struggled to find a diagnosis. Our progress, in retrospect, had been steady, though slow. We had started with the established medical system, then begun to experiment with alternative therapies and, finally, crossed over to a world of therapies unknown to the average citizen of the United States. Looking back, I could see an educational process at work which had broken down old mind-sets. We were building new intellectual filters with which to process information.

At the moment I was trying to understand the Computron and how it might work. Clearly, this piece of equipment was remarkable in its ability to see past symptoms and find causes. Obviously, the skill of the operator was important, as Doug Leber had demonstrated through several hours of finding and probing the acupuncture points on Linda's swollen fingers and feet. There was the possibility, too, that the operator of the Computron needed sensitivity that was supernormal in order to divine all of the answers.

The Computron reminded me of a primitive form of the small hand-held device [tricorder] used by the doctor on Star Trek, the difference being the amount of time taken to complete the test.

This time factor explained why a medical doctor would not be too interested in using a Computron. Granted, our cost of $500 for the diagnosis was significant. But the time involved was five and one-half hours—less than $100 per hour for Doug's time. Most medical doctors can book well in excess of $100 per hour.

The Computron was an amazing instrument, and I resolved to learn more about it. First, however, we needed to deal with geopathic stress. As soon as we returned to Ashland, I called Mr. Mechem. He was well and ready to dowse.

Mr. Mechem arrived on the 8th of January and walked briskly into our house. He was distinguished-looking and had a deep, resonant voice. His white hair was combed back. He wore gold-rimmed glasses, and his neatly pressed, long-sleeved shirt was cinched at the collar by a bolo tie with a large piece of picture jasper. Mr. Mechem carried a very nice leather briefcase, and after introductions, invited us to sit at the dining room table. Linda sat on one side and I sat on the other.

"What do you know about dowsing?" he asked in his rich voice. It was the voice of a minister or radio announcer and made him seem much younger than his age, which I later learned was seventy-nine.

"We don't know much," I told him.

"Well, anybody can dowse and I'm going to teach you how right now. You can dowse for just about anything, you know," he said, opening the briefcase and revealing an assortment of meters, gauges, and dowsing instruments. "Some people think it's the work of the devil. It's not. It's just another sense we were born with like sight or hearing, or smell or taste. We need to develop our ability. I figure I've been given the right to keep this hot old body going any way I want. If dowsing works, I'm going to use it."

"How did you learn to dowse?" asked Linda.

"I was an engineer for Douglas Aircraft for thirty years," he said. "At the end of my career I was running a plant working on the Space Lab. Had forty-two engineers and four hundred shop people. We were doing some remodeling and had to locate underground pipes. I bought some very sophisticated metal detection equipment to find these. I was in my office one day and looked out the window toward this area where we were adding on and saw one of the fellows with a forked stick, a water witch, looking for the underground pipes. I called him in and asked him why he wasn't using the equipment we bought. He told me he could do a better job witching for it. He could too. I decided I was going to learn about this, and when my wife and I retired to Medford, I took up a study of it. Now here's the interesting thing about dowsing. Just about everyone in this country believes in water witchers. The reason is they've had some experience with it. They know someone who witches or dowses for water, or they've heard about someone who found a well that way. The most conservative old Bible-reading farmer in the country will call for a dowser if he needs a new well, or he'll cut a switch from a willow and dowse it himself. He doesn't stop to think for a minute what pulls that switch down so hard that sometimes it peels the bark right off. Yet if I tell him I can dowse for a lost person, or figure out what vitamins my body needs, or tell you if two people are compatible by using a pendulum, that old farmer will probably say "work of the devil." But what makes that willow switch point to the ground when that farmer stands over a water vein?"

Mr. Mechem stopped talking and pulled out a black pocket comb and combed his hair using his left hand as a guide.

"I don't know exactly, either," he said. "But it bloody well works. Everything gives off rays like electricity or magnetism and, using the pendulum and concentrating, you can find the rays you're looking for and measure them. No one can explain electricity either, you know. We've just learned how to use it. Now let's get started making you two into dowsers."

He reached into his briefcase and pulled out a pair of brass rods that were bent on the end and handed them to Linda.

"These are L-Rods," he told her. "Hold the small end in your hands and let the long part point out in front of you. Let it drop down just a little bit. That's right. Now stand up and lead me to that bad bedroom."

Linda got up and turned zombie-like holding the L-Rods uncomfortably in front of her and walked stiffly toward the bedroom.

"There's a water vein in there, just like I told you on the phone," said Mechem. "Concentrate on that water vein and walk slowly into the bedroom. When you reach that vein, those L-Rods will cross."

Mr. Mechem was behind Linda. He was holding a metal wand about two feet long, which he pointed different directions and wiggled. I followed Mr. Mechem and, in single file, we entered the bedroom. As she reached the spot where her head used to rest before we moved the bed, the L-Rods swung violently toward each other and crossed.

"Aha!" screamed Linda.

I took the L-Rods and they seemed to work for me too, but since I already knew where the "hot spot" was in our bedroom, I thought I could be making the rods cross. It didn't take much of an intentional movement to make them turn toward each other.

"Meech" led us back to the table and removed a couple of pamphlets, some laminated cards, and a small plastic vial which contained a pendulum. The pendulum was a piece of lead shaped like a tiny beet. It dangled from a six-inch length of blue string. He handed me the pendulum.

"You can have this one and keep the L-Rods too. Play with them. The first thing you have to do is program your pendulum. Different gyrations of the pendulum mean different things to different people. A clockwise movement can indicate 'yes'—counter-clockwise—a 'no.' I like to have a 'yes' be a back-and-forth movement like nodding your head yes, with a side-to-side swing to the pendulum meaning 'no.' Just take a minute and program your instrument."

I swung the pendulum concentrating on 'yes,' then moved it side-to-side, thinking "this means 'no.'" It was very easy to move the pendulum. Subtle, almost indiscernible movements could cause it to change directions.

"What makes it move?" I asked Mechem.

"Your subconscious mind provides involuntary muscle move-ments which make the pendulum move. The pendulum is a device for communicating with the subconscious. The limitation is that you get only yes-and-no answers. This means a dowser has to carefully construct a series of questions in order to get the infor-mation he needs. You can get all mixed up if your questions aren't clear and precise. When I was map dowsing for some wells recently, I found three spots on the property which I thought might give water. I went out there and dowsed them in person and told the contractor which one I thought was best. He drilled and didn't find anything. He called me up and said, 'Meech, you're off your gourdy-gourd here. There ain't no water.' I pulled that map out again to figure out what I'd done wrong and discovered I hadn't asked for north. I was oriented wrong. I forgot to ask a key question."

He held up his pendulum which looked like a tiny twisted silver carrot on a heavy chain. "This thing tells all. . .well. . .sometimes," he told us. "But you need to have a relaxed mind, you have to concentrate, and you have to formulate clear questions that proceed logically."

"Meech" held his pendulum up in front of us and swung it back and forth.

"Hold it with a light grip," he said. "And don't cross your legs." Information came at us in a torrent. He showed how to test for vitamin surpluses and deficiencies, how to ask for the proper dosage, and how often to take them. He showed us how to test for compatibility between couples, between teachers and students, or between animals and people. He grabbed the phone book and opened to the Yellow Pages to demonstrate how he would find a doctor or a plumber. He pointed to the names one at a time asking himself, "Would I have a compatible relationship with this individual?" His pendulum would gyrate 'yes' or 'no.'

I watched his hand and fingers closely, and it appeared to me that there was a very noticeable movement to change directions. Whether this was voluntary or involuntary I didn't know. With Mechem, however, I was once again in a suspension of disbelief. He had, after all, used a map and his pendulum to tell us we had a water vein and magnetic grid line in the bedroom in exactly the same location as Doug Leber and Joyce had placed them.

Mr. Mechem enjoyed being a teacher, and he put us through our paces. Very quickly we were writing down names of couples we knew, to see what the pendulum would reveal about their compatibility. I could tell right away that Linda was a more sensitive dowser. She just let it happen. I tried to second-guess the pendulum and, as a result, influenced the outcome.

"If you want to learn more," said Mechem, "the Southern Oregon Society of Dowsers puts on a workshop every once in a while where we take you through all this a bit more slowly."

Wouldn't you know it, I thought to myself. In America there's an organization for everything. There's probably a magazine too.

"If you want more detail," Mr. Mechem continued, "join the American Society of Dowsers. Costs $25 per year and they put out a nice quarterly magazine. But, now I've got to go to work and get you straightened out so Linda can start getting well."

From a folder in his briefcase he removed a copy of the floor plan of our house which I had mailed to him. The diagram of the house was overlaid with coded lines and areas denoted with hatch marks. The lines represented water veins, fault lines, magnetic grids, and sixty-cycle harmonics. The hatch marks were for vortices, hot spots, and good energy areas. It was encouraging to see that most of the living room and the middle bedroom were good energy areas. There were two water veins running under the house.

Curiously, they were on nearly parallel courses, bending and straightening out at the same time.

Mr. Mechem started with the mundane. He checked all the electrical outlets with a standard voltmeter. He explained that electromagnetic zones could, over long periods of exposure, cause serious illnesses such as cancer. He found no significant problems with any of our outlets or appliances. There was, however, the problem of the sixty-cycle harmonic in the kitchen. Mr. Mechem used his Gauss meter and then his metal wand to determine the shape and source of the harmonic. The wand, he told us, worked just like a pendulum. He unwrapped a package of small kitchen magnets and placed several on the bottom of the stove and along the baseboard. He dowsed again. The sixty-cycle harmonic had disappeared.

"It's gone," he said confidently. "Well, it's not really gone. We just deflected it outside where it can't hurt anything. We can't get rid of these noxious energies but they can be dispersed or deflected. I use magnets and iron rods. Some people use crystals. Others use copper wire in loops. No one in this country except the American Society of Dowsers is doing any research on these problems. There's lots of research in Germany. The government even supports it there. The Germans found in some of the old houses where the same family has lived for four hundred years, that a person in each generation has died of some cancer-like disease. When they dowsed it they found noxious energies. These energy fields come from geological rock faults in the earth's crust, from mineral deposits, and from underground streams. There's also a system of grid lines which envelop the earth—the Hartman Grid and the Curry Grid. These energy waves are at frequencies of X-rays and gamma rays. When the water veins or fault lines or magnetic grid lines cross, there's an increase in energy—a hot spot. It can make you sick and keep you sick."

While he was talking "Meech" walked back and forth, following fault lines and water veins from where they entered our living space to where they exited. He made no notes but a week later sent us a two-page written report—Report #0224. In the report he detailed what he had found and what he had done. He concluded as follows:

"The master bedroom bed had a high rate of geopathogenic energy at one time and was detrimental to the occupant. . .this in the form of magnetic grid, coupled with water veins and some stray sixty-cycle energies, did produce detrimental biological disturbances. New location of the bed now seems to be in a good energy zone beneficial to occupants. Elimination of kitchen noxious zones and outside power sixty-cycle harmonics should likewise benefit occupants. Due to location in hills no RF (radio frequencies—TV, FM, etc.) were identified throughout the house."

Before he packed up and left "Meech" went to his car, opened the trunk, and got a can of spray powder to mark certain spots outside. It was chilly and he put on his jacket and a jaunty tweed-brimmed hat.

"Doctor says I need to wear this damn hat until I get completely rid of this cold," he told me confidentially.

I followed him around the house as he dowsed for points at which to pound iron bars into the earth which would deflect harmful energies. He marked two spots and then we went back inside to settle up. I wrote him a check for $50. Mr. Mechem wasn't in it for the money. We said our good-byes and thanked him profusely, totally confident that he had cleared us up—certain that the noxious demons had been exorcised. T. E. Mechem had been entered in our gallery of heroes.

Later, I walked down the hill to the old railroad switchyard and found a couple of railroad spikes. As soon as I returned home, puffing from the walk up the steep hill, I pounded those spikes into the marked spots, completing the diversion of energies away from our house.

Dowsing was a fascinating but nearly imponderable subject for me. I played with the pendulum and had some early success. I found my lost keys, which were in the middle of a huge pile of clean clothes. Linda was as impressed as I was surprised. She accepted me as an accomplished dowser based on this one brief, unrepeated example, and when she was into her agonies I would get the pendulum and dowse for answers to her questions: "When will this headache go away?" "When will Doug Leber's homeopathic remedies arrive?"

I did well on the headaches but never could come up with the answer as to when Doug Leber's medicine, which we saw as the final solution to her problems, would be walked up to our door by the UPS delivery person.

In this interval I started the task of locating a suitable dentist, a member of the Academy of Biological Dentistry, to cavitate the infection in Linda's jaw. There were very few choices. Apparently, not many dentists were biologically oriented. The membership of that association was small. Fortunately, there were choices in the Seattle area and in Phoenix; fortunate, because my parents lived north of Seattle and Linda's lived near Phoenix. We would have places to stay which would reduce the ever-growing cost of our adventures. We decided on Arizona. We owed her parents a visit and it would be warmer. We made an appointment with Dr. Terry Lee for January 27, 1994. Dr. Lee had been referred to us by the office of Dr. Arana–the president of the Association of Biological Dentistry. I also talked to the recommended dentist in Seattle. All of them were familiar with the work of Doug Leber. "He's never been wrong. . .," Dr. Arana's assistant told me. Obviously, Leber wasn't operating in a vacuum. A few professionals were quite familiar with his work.

We had three weeks of January to kill. Linda turned up the heat and buried herself under comforters. I went looking for books on dowsing. I read the ones that Mr. Mechem had recommended. They seemed lightweight, almost frivolous. Dowsing was, if not magical, at least unexplainable. I wanted a rational explanation. In a used book store I was attracted to a book called *The Essential T. C. Lethbridge.* I was drawn to the dust cover, which appeared to represent an array of round pendulums on long strings. I bought the book and went to school. Lethbridge was a noted British archeologist. He had a distinguished career as director of excavations for the Cambridge Antiquarian Society and for the University Museum of Archaeology and Ethnology. He was, thus, a scientist and approached his personal study of dowsing with a scientific attitude. In the last ten years of his life, he wrote ten short books describing the details of his investigations.

Lethbridge, unlike most dowsers, used a long pendulum–a ball of wood on a length of string which he wound around a pencil. He soon discovered that he would get a pendulum reaction to different substances at different string lengths. Iron, for example, caused the pendulum to rotate at a string length of 32 inches. He would lower his pendulum over a substance to be tested, letting the pendulum move back and forth. With iron, when he had let out exactly 32 inches of string, the pendulum would begin to rotate.

He had discovered a "rate" and was able to predict what he would find in an archaeological dig by using his pendulum over the dig site. He could, in fact, find substances by pointing the finger of his left hand and moving it in all directions. When the finger pointed in a line with the substance, the pendulum would react. "Improbable though it may seem," wrote Mr. Lethbridge, "this apparently strange operation does work. The dowser is using a primitive scientific instrument; one might describe it almost as a kind of radar. . ."

Lethbridge offered a theory of why dowsing works: ". . .each substance obviously has an electromagnetic field force, which is discernible with a pendulum with the correct length of string. . .If the balls and pendulums were standardized, a complete table of rates could be worked out, which would always be constant. . .it will not work by itself. It needs the human body, or rather the human electromagnetic field, to make it work. This supplies the current and turns it into a machine. . .It may be that each person might have to work out his own table of rates according to the potential of his field, in the same way that each person according to. . .his eyesight has to vary the focus of the eyepieces of his binoculars."

Was dowsing magic? Lethbridge, the scientist, said "no." He believed that recognizing that each individual could develop a repeatable standard table of rates ". . .lifts the subject of dowsing out of the world of magic, straight into the realm of physics."

Lethbridge's experiments are detailed in his book and could be repeated by anyone with the patience and the time. After a long series of experiments he concluded that the radiations of substances were cone-shaped and that ". . .each cone may in reality be drawn out into a single thin ray. If so, the ascending ray probably passes out into space, while the descending one extends to the magnetic center of the earth. . .A perfectly fantastic 'science fiction' world is beginning to emerge from our simple study. The whole surface (of the earth) must be covered with invisible and interlocking cones. Since such things as streams and water pipes also have their fields, these must be high walls, curving or straight, which pass through the mass of cones."

The dowser's personal energy field extends, then, through this mass of cones, responding to the field of the object being sought, using the instrument of the pendulum. "It seems that our electromagnetic field. . .can project a ray to an unlimited distance, through a forest of other ascending rays, and will. . .single out a particular ray and record it by gyration of the pendulum."

Is this any more fantastical than a radio or television set being able to tune in a particular signal out of the thousands of such signals which fill the space in our houses at any given moment?

"Again and again," said Lethbridge, "I have to stress that I approach all this with complete disbelief."

Lethbridge then apparently shocked himself that the pendulum, in addition to responding to physical objects, would also react to ideas or concepts. For example, he learned that he could determine the sex of fossils. There was a rate for male and for female. Subsequently, using the pendulum he could determine the sex of anything. Male was 24 inches; female 29 inches. The fact that an indication of maleness or femaleness remained in the electromagnetic field of a fossil after 100 million years led him to some serious metaphysical pondering:

"'Unless you become again as little children ye cannot enter the kingdom of heaven'. . .Unless you can appreciate that there is a part of your makeup which lasts indefinitely and knows much more that your brain, you are stuck in the world of materialism and atom bombs. But if you can appreciate that this something exists, a completely new view of life opens up. We can regard our body as a caterpillar and expect to go on through a chrysalis state to that of an imago, or complete eternity. For the whole is the sum of its parts. If part of the whole persists for 100 million years, the whole must do so too. We must try to find what else can be transferred to the electromagnetic field in order to see what might survive indefinitely."

This led him through a series of experiments involving sling-shot pebbles used by prehistoric armies. Could information from one electromagnetic field be imparted and held by another electromagnetic field over a period of years? With his experiment using beach stones found at ancient fortresses, Lethbridge begins to explain how a "sensitive" might be able to touch an object and from it give information about the life of its owners:

"To avoid handling, a number of pebbles of suitable walnut size were picked up from the shingle on the beach with a pair of tongs and immediately dropped into a container. They were never touched by hand. When tested with the pendulum, none of them gave any reaction except the 14 inches for silica. How did the other rates for thought and male sex become attached to other similar pebbles, which man had handled perhaps two thousand years ago?

"I took one of the untouched pebbles and held it in my hand for half an hour. Then I tested it (with a pendulum). It gave the 14-inch rate for silica as before; but now it reacted to the 27-inch rate for thought as well. There was no sex rate as there was with the sling stones. I thought it over for some time. Perhaps the male rate was induced in the field of the object by some feeling of violence on the part of the slinger. I took a pebble out into the garden and flung it as hard as I could against a stone wall. I picked it up and tested it again. It now reacted to 14, 24, and 27 inches. My violence had apparently induced my sex rate into the field of the pebble. Of course the term 'sex rate' may well be incorrect. It is simply a term of convenience. It is a rate common to males when it is 24 inches and to females when it is 29, and it is different from what I am calling a thought rate of 27 inches. Memory, as distinct from thought, is 7 inches. 20 inches is the rate for living things. Thought (27) on the pendulum appears to memory plus life (20 + 7). The experiment was then repeated by my wife. She took two untouched pebbles and threw them in turn against the wall. When examined they reacted both to the 27-inch thought rate and to the rate for the female sex. They would not react to the male rate.

"I then took half a dozen supposed sling-stones from Wandlebury (a prehistoric fortress). Of course these had been excavated and picked up by man. If the thought rate is easily induced, one might expect them to have a 14-inch rate for silica and perhaps 27 inches for thought from the modern excavators who dug them up. But they should not have a 24-inch rate because this is apparently only induced by violent treatment. All six pebbles reacted to 14, 24, and 27 inches. Violence had apparently had its effect on them and as we had not treated them violently, it seemed that this 24-inch male sex rate must have come from the prehistoric slinger and have been with each pebble for two thousand years or so."

Throughout history, objects containing information or power imparted to them have been used as talismans. If one can accept the result of Lethbridge's experiments, it is no great leap to accept the possibility that a healer could impart his or her energy to the energy field of an object which might assist with healing. The notion that we all give off rays of energy which can be sensed by someone tuned to those vibrations opens exciting possibilities for diagnosis and healing. I read in a book on dowsing about people who, using their pendulum, could, by asking a series of medically-related questions, diagnose health problems and offer remedies for relief.

I was getting lost in this maze of new information until, once again in the local bookstore, my hand reached out and touched a copy of *Vibrational Medicine* by Richard Gerber, M.D. This very comprehensive piece of work, by a medical doctor no less, became the primary textbook for all my further studies. If I had found it any sooner I would not have understood a word of it. At this point, however, I was ready to deal with some bold new concepts.

I purchased *Vibrational Medicine* because it had a chapter on electroacupuncture machines. This was the type of machine used by Doug Leber. EAV (electroacupuncture according to Voll) was a technology invented by a German neurosurgeon in the 1940s. Dr. Reinhard Voll's machine, the Dermatron, measures the electrical parameters of acupuncture points which are displayed on voltmeter readouts. In his research Dr. Voll had established norms for each acupoint. A reading above or below the norm would indicate to the operator of the machine that a particular organ or organ system was out of whack—either degenerative or inflamed.

Doug Leber's machine, the Computron, is clearly a computerized Dermatron with the computer facilitating a quicker inventory of the body's functions. According to Dr. Gerber, EAV equipment has "the ability to measure electromagnetic disturbances in the meridian system and to find imbalances in the flow of ch'i. This, in turn, allows one to detect cellular pathology in a particular area of the body as well as to predict future organic dysfunction."

It was quite remarkable to read a book by a medical doctor which validated the effectiveness of not only the Computron but of acupuncture, homeopathy, Bach remedies, and even crystals. Dr. Gerber not only validated these healing systems but provided a scientific rationale, suggesting that they were not dissimilar from certain routine medical systems such as magnetic resonance imaging (MRI). An MRI scan is based on the analysis of biological resonance. Resonance is caused by electrons circling a nucleus in defined orbits. The orbits have a certain frequency and vibrate at a certain rate. By applying energy of a proper frequency, an electron can be excited into moving to a higher energy level in its orbit. Gerber says, "Although the energetic level of humans varies from moment to moment and day to day, the body tends to vibrate at a particular frequency."

In high school physics we were taught the Einsteinian view that matter is not solid. $E=mc^2$ means that matter and energy are the same thing. A rock is not, in reality, solid. It just vibrates at a different frequency than, say, water or the human body. A rock is composed of the same building blocks, electrons and atoms, as is any other matter, and on a microcosmic level contains spaces between atom and electron which are mathematically relational to the distances between the sun and the earth. There is a universal substance. "In the beginning was the Word and the Word was made flesh." The universal substance is that energy or vibration, that Word or sound of which everything is composed. Matter is crystallized energy. It is frozen light.

Mr. Mechem and T. C. Lethbridge, using their respective pendulum techniques, are able to measure, or at least locate, different vibrational rates. Dr. Voll or Doug Leber, using the Dermatron or Computron, are able to do the same. A medical technician using an MRI scanner measures the resonance of certain atoms, which provides the physician with a detailed picture of the human body.

A homeopathic practitioner matches the frequency of the remedy to boost the frequency of electron orbits which are in disease. Gerber's thesis was essentially the same as outlined in less scientific detail by Fred Epping at the beginning of our Qigong class—we are energy bodies surrounded by other energy bodies and miscellaneous fields of energy.

We are energy; energy flows through us and around us. We are held together in a physical sense by patterns of energy. A smooth flow of energy through our systems is important to wellness. Blockages of energy are impediments to wellness. Energy flows in certain patterns or channels (the meridians) and enters and exits out physical bodies via chakras. Gerber suggests that the planet Earth has a meridian system of its own, consisting of a grid work of energy channels. Dr. Gerber writes, "If. . .living organisms are entrained by the planetary field that they live in, there are probably beneficial as well as detrimental effects of particular patterns and types of local energy fields. . .Studies in Germany and England have produced evidence which suggests that geopathic stress may not only contribute to the production of illness, but that stresses may hinder the effective treatment of diseases as well." Doug Leber had told us that Linda's blood was in "left spin." Gerber points out that researchers, using a device like the Voll Machine, have discovered that certain molecules of blood rotate in a clockwise or counterclockwise direction. "It has been found," reports Dr. Gerber, "that individuals living in regions associated with geopathic stress tended to have counterclockwise (left) rotational polarity in their blood." Left spin, it was further discovered, opposes therapy with vibrational medicines. "A. . .majority of patients with cancer possess this counterclockwise blood polarity."

We were a long way from the emergency room at St. Vincent's Hospital in Santa Fe. If someone had suggested that in the intervening fourteen months, in an attempt to be well, Linda would get acupuncture, intravenous vitamins, be wrapped in hot and cold towels, take wheatgrass juice enemas, receive rectally-administered ozone, ingest all manner of vitamins and supplements, sleep on a biocircuit, calm herself with flower essences, drink various herbal concoctions, move her bed and pound iron bars into the earth to avoid harmful rays, find out that her blood was spinning to the left, and learn that the proximate cause of her ailments was an infected jaw, we would have been incredulous.

Vibrational Medicine articulated our postgraduate education in healing modalities. Dr. Gerber likewise crystallized our own world view. Education is, after all, a function of experience. A learning curve is certainly more dramatic when one is under pressure—particularly the pressure to survive. Our education was coming into focus.

The body is more than just a machine. A healer needs to offer more than a plumbing service. Surgery and pharmaceuticals are just different methods of plumbing. There is, in fact, more to the body than the physical self which dominated our attention. There is also mind and soul. If the physical body is crystallized light (energy at a slower vibration), it is likely that we have other bodies like a mental body and soul body which vibrate at frequencies above those of visible light. These other bodies, be they etheric, astral, or mental, are logically connected to the physical body mechanisms (chakras) which step down the vibration of energy and conduct it through the body along pathways (meridians). A healthy entity will be one which has all of its energy bodies functioning in balance. This balance, however, can be disturbed by many forces including internal and external forces. The mind, for example, is an internal force which can affect the smooth flow of energy. Negative thoughts can be manifested as pathological conditions in the cellular body. If one of the subtle bodies is damaged by vibrational energy from radiation, this can ultimately affect the health of the physical body. As Dr. Bach suggested, the seeds of disease may be sown first by vibrational disturbance in one of our higher energy bodies. A measuring device which can read these vibrations will be able to predict conditions before they become pathological in the physical body. A sensitive dowser should be able to note abnormal conditions from the vibrations given off by dysfunctional organs or organ systems. A homeopathic remedy or flower essence which contains only a vibrational imprint of its original substance can, through resonance, change the level of disease by moving vibrations back to their correct rate. These changes could occur in any of our energy bodies which, in all likelihood, are like a blueprint for our physical body, containing the master plan for our physical development. If we are energy, then, as Dr. Gerber says, ". . .we can be affected by energy."

Vibrational medicine, if effective, would have none of the harmful side effects of chemotherapy (drugs) or surgery. In Doug Leber's view, however, there is a time and a place for surgery. So, we packed and prepared to drive south, waiting for a break in the weather that would allow us easy passage over the Siskiyou Mountains into that long day's drive known as California.

Chapter 17
Cavitation Surgery

The first day we made it to Tehachapi, arriving after dark. Our dinner was in the hamper. We often carried food on trips, because of the difficulty of finding suitable vegetarian fare along the road. I had made rice balls, brown rice covered with toasted nori (seaweed) and filled with a dab of umeboshi plum paste. A macrobiotic treat. Tasty, filling, nourishing, and complete. Six hundred miles of Interstate 5 had, as always, left us vibrating and uneasy. We ate, watched TV, and showered. Then we spread our silk biocircuits out on the bed and slipped our feet and hands into them. Sleep came quickly.

I woke refreshed, ate rice cakes with tahini and jam, and made juice and fruit for Linda. Loaded, checked out, and back in the car, we headed for a day in the desert on the dry road to Arizona. The highlight of the morning was the wind farms on the ridge between Tehachapi and Mojave—testimony to a future of capturing energy from the air and a twirling memory of the nearly forgotten investment tax credits of the 1980s.

Our intended route had been through Los Angeles but a week before, the big earthquake had hit the San Fernando Valley—a violent form of geopathic stress. Traffic from Bakersfield was being diverted to Four Corners and Barstow. The highway was thick with trucks, and at Four Corners entrepreneurs had already set up along the roadside selling necessities to travelers trying to get out of or back into the Los Angeles basin. Linda wanted a piece of fruit, so I hit the brakes and backed up to where an Angeleno was selling large navel oranges. He sold me the single orange I requested for fifty cents while reeling off significant engine and transmission specifications of the car I was driving.

"It's a nice engine," he concluded. "Nice."

Linda ate her orange a section at a time while wearing the yellow glasses Doug Leber had prescribed. Color was another vibrational therapy widely used by alternative practitioners. It wasn't new. In 1878 an American physician, Dr. Edwin Babbitt, wrote a book called *The Principles of Light and Color.* Babbitt claimed that yellow, for example, could help bronchitis, liver ailments and constipation.

We learned in grade school, using a prism, that light can be divided into different colors because those colors have different wave lengths. Colors have different wave frequencies and vibrate at different rates. Those rates can be matched to different areas of the body, and the energy of color can be used to resonate with the body's systems to boost improper or diseased vibrations back into their correct energy orbit. In Eastern thought the physical body is connected to the etheric body by seven chakras, which are spinning focal points of energy. The chakras are like transformers which move energy into the physical body via the endocrine glands. Violet, for example, vibrates at the rate of the pineal gland, blue with the thyroid, and red with the adrenals. According to the doctrine of color therapy, color entering the eyes is directed to the hypothalamus gland, to the pineal, and on to the pituitary gland—the regulator of hormones in the body.

It is not too difficult for a layman to accept the healing possibilities of color. We react strongly and positively to the color of sky and forest, often feeling uplifted and energized. A putrid paint scheme in a school or office, however, can have the opposite effect. The desert was an excellent place for color therapy, with or without glasses. Blue sky, beige sand, red and orange rocks, green Joshua trees whizzed by at 80 mph as we sped through the desert of Southeastern California.

Later that evening we circled to the north of Phoenix through the saguaros forests, watching light reflecting from boulders and picture windows, then turned south on Scottsdale Road. The glow from the oasis of Phoenix lay ahead—a megalopolis of four-lane arterials, shopping centers, and planned developments. I had been born in Phoenix in 1942, when the wartime population swelled to 50,000. In 1994, Arizona State University could boast a student body of 50,000 and our small adobe house, long bulldozed, which had sat on the edge of town, would now be at the city center. The sprawl now enclosed the expensive real estate of Paradise Valley, once dry as a bone and available, my dad claimed, at $10 an acre.

Linda's parents' home was in Fountain Hills, which was separated from Scottsdale by a cactus-covered ridge and the southwestern branch of the Mayo Clinic. The Clinic, when we had passed it two years earlier, seemed all alone. It was now being surrounded by development. Build it and they will come. They will come with Medicare and Medicare supplements and HMO's and corporate medical and wellness plans.

We arrived after dark, unloaded, and ate. Linda was tired but feeling surprisingly well. She took an H_2O_2 bath and went to bed.

In the morning I walked the short distance to the artificial lake with the water cannon fountain, which is the centerpiece of the planned real estate development of Fountain Hills. Groups of people in running outfits, jackets, and pants, were walking around the lake. There was not, as I had hoped to find, an inconspicuous hideaway around the grassy shores of Lake Fountain Hills, so I settled for a flat spot and began my Qigong exercises as had been my daily habit for several months. Shortly before leaving we had finished our class on part two of the form, and I was now equipped with a new array of twists, stretches, bends, and arm flapping designed, Fred told us, to move the ch'i in and out of our bodies. I went into my routine in full view of the walkers, and over the three weeks we stayed in Fountain Hills generated no noticeable curiosity.

I had recently read an article about a scientist in China who, using electroacoustics, had discovered that high-frequency acoustical waves were emitted by the hands of Qigong masters. These waves of energy were 100 times more powerful than those of the average individual. The professor then built a machine to duplicate this sound and tested it on more than a thousand patients. He recorded pain reduction, improved circulation, muscular relaxation, and alleviation of depression. He received awards from the Chinese Ministry of Health. It is not unknown in China for Qigong Masters to use their own ch'i to stimulate healing in others.

On the last night of our class, Fred had followed me out to the car and handed me a small, polished stone. "Give this to Linda," he said. "What is it?" I had asked. "Just have her hold it or put it in her pocket and see if it helps."

I flapped my wings in the final sequence of the Wild Goose Qigong exercise, altering my neurochemistry profile, enhancing the efficiency of my immune system, increasing cell metabolism, moderating the function of my endocrine system, and I thought about healing rocks and T. C. Lethbridge, while the gray-headed walkers circled the large wastewater pond and a water cannon shot a stream of gray water hundreds of feet into the air. A light breeze drifted nasty droplets which covered the windows of stucco-sided condos on the perimeter of the lake.

Before we left Ashland I had called Doug Leber's office and asked him to mail the remedies he had promised to Linda's parents' address. And, at the request of Dr. Lee, I had asked Leber to fax a copy of the EAV printout, which we had not yet received, to Dr. Lee's office in Phoenix. By the time of our appointment on January 27, 1994, the remedies had not arrived and the fax had not been sent.

Though Linda was not looking forward to surgery, she was certain that it would be helpful. Camelback Dentistry was just inside the Phoenix City limits on the Scottsdale side. Traffic runs smoothly on the four-lane arterials of Scottsdale and Phoenix. But it still took over forty minutes to make the drive. The office appeared to be a type of cooperative arrangement with several dentists sharing space. Over a three-week period, I got the idea that Dr. Lee was the only dentist in the building practicing biological dentistry. I got this idea because when he talked about mercury amalgams, root canals, and cavitation surgery, he tended to whisper. There were no private offices in this practice—only work stations which were completely open to view. In January of 1994, all we knew about biological dentistry was that Doug Leber, diagnostician extraordinaire, had recommended it. Thus, it was comforting to see, when I first had a chance to visit Dr. Lee's work area, that he had one of Doug's Computron machines. The EAV report, as I mentioned, had not arrived. Dr. Lee took some X-rays, couldn't see the abscesses, but assumed Leber was correct. He had worked on patients referred by Doug Leber before and testified, as had Dr. Arana's office, that Leber had never been wrong. While Linda underwent surgery I took a couple of books and other reading material provided by Dr. Lee and set about studying. I learned quite a bit. The surgery took three hours.

What we were probably dealing with was a condition called NICO—"neuralgia-inducing cavitational osteonecrosis"—which was a pocket of infection located in the jawbone above or below a tooth. Often there were several of these pockets or cavitations connected by fistulas. These cavitations in the bone were full of dying or dead bone and marrow. All this material contained infection. Bacteria and toxins were slowly leaking into the system, causing a depression of the immune system. Dr. Lee had handed me a brand new book titled *Root Canal Cover-Up Exposed*. It was written by George E. Meinig, D.D.S. who was a "founding member of the American Association of Endodontists (root canal therapists)." Dr. Meinig had spent a career doing root canals. Dr. Meinig claims that in 1993, 24 million American teeth were root canaled. The good dentist now claims that root canals are unhealthy. They are unhealthy, because the roots of the tooth cannot be completely disinfected. All the bacteria living in our mouths cannot be completely eradicated. Thus, bacteria becomes trapped in the dentin of the tooth. The toxins produced by these bacteria escape through the dentin into the tubials and the bacteria themselves could escape into the bloodstream "through minuscule spaces or porosity of the root canal filling material." These particular bacteria thrive in the absence of oxygen and become more virulent and their toxins more toxic. If a person's immune system is strong, the body can keep this infection localized. With a weak immune system, the tissue at the end of the roots cannot control the organism, and the infection moves through the bloodstream to other organs of the body.

The problem occurs because dental science has not yet perfected the technique of creating a filling which will completely seal the roots to their tip. Part of this problem is caused by shrinkage of the filling material after the procedure is completed.

Dr. Meinig's bottom line: "Root canal fillings can cause serious side effects."

The shocking revelation in the book, however, is that Dr. Meinig's information on root canals comes from studies done by a Weston A. Price, D.D.S, M.S., F.A.C.D., chief scientist for the American Dental Association and published in 1923! So what happened to this research? Dr. Meinig explains as follows:

"How could scientific discoveries as important as these be so completely suppressed? Two or three factors were mainly respon- sible.

"First, all during the time of the Price research there was an intense disagreement among members of both the medical and dental professions as to whether or not the focal theory of infection was valid.

". . .this theory contends that infected teeth, tonsils, tonsil tags, and similar other areas that are infected could be responsible for setting up a whole new infection in another tissue or organ of the body because the bacteria involved are transported to the new area via the bloodstream. The views, both pro and con, were fiercely debated and resulted in professional wars—that is, between physicians and their medical societies; between dentists and dental societies; between physicians and dentists; and between dentists and physicians. The arguments of believers and nonbelievers were hot and heavy. These arguments against the acceptance of the theory created a milieu that was not readily receptive to Dr. Price's research results.

"Acceptance today of focal infection is so taken for granted that hardly anyone pays any attention to it. . .Keep in mind that such arguments about new ideas among doctors are numerous. New theories have a way of stimulating autocratic oppressive behavior that unfortunately stifles the advancement of medicine."

Dr. Meinig points out that when penicillin was developed, there arose a belief that antibiotics could cure all these problems (infections), and little is heard today about focal infections.

As reported by Dr. Meinig on p. 111/112 of *Root Canal Cover-Up Exposed,* Dr. Weston Price summarized his own findings as follows:

"People are not living to the entire span of life which they have a right to expect.

"Death is occurring even in our most civilized communities largely from the degenerative diseases chief of which is heart disease.

"It is practically, if not entirely, a physical impossibility to sterilize infected cementum by treating through the dentin. It is like trying to sterilize infection in the label on the bottle by putting disinfectants in the bottle.

"Root fillings do not continue to fill root canals. The amount of space that ultimately develops is approximately the amount of solvent that was used with the root-filling material, assuming that mechanical filling of every area was possible.

"Individuals are not comparable in their defense against degenerative diseases. Some are susceptible and must have an entirely different preventive program.

"The degenerative diseases are largely symptoms of degenerative processes in the bloodstream, an important contributing cause for which is long continued, usually unsuspected, chronic infection.

". . .(X-rays) cannot reveal all the required information, and under old standards will often be misleading.

"Chronic dental infections can produce antigens, to which the sensitized patient may respond with an allergy of severe and very obscure type.

"Dental infections can be demonstrated to have had specific localizing ability for many of the organs and tissues of the body....

"We cannot, therefore continue in the light of these new truths to give any quarter to the infected pulpless tooth until we can both accomplish its disinfection and insure its continued sterility."

On the wall of Dr. Lee's office was a huge chart showing a line of teeth with diagrammatic connections to all organs and systems of the body. This was labeled, "The Energetic Relations of Teeth with Respect to Organs and Tissue Systems," by—guess who—Dr. Reinhard Voll, the developer of electroacupuncture diagnosis. As a part of his electroacupuncture studies Dr. Voll discovered, as far back as the 1950s, that each tooth is in circuit with an acupuncture meridian. If a certain tooth became infected, organs on the same meridian could also become diseased. Dr. Price's research concluded that infected teeth could cause heart, kidney, and endocrine diseases. Price claimed that if these root canals were extracted, many chronic health problems would be resolved.

It was kind of like the old song about the thigh bone connected to the leg bone, but in Linda's case, her infected teeth bones, according to Voll, were connected to her thyroid, spleen, stomach, her parathyroid, anterior pituitary lobe, sacroiliac joint, and several other parts of her body.

It was difficult to digest these many revelations in such a short period. Dentistry has been universally acclaimed for eliminating tooth decay. I had many times touted the work of dentistry, suggesting they would soon put themselves out of business. But the material I was reading indicated that dentistry was making people sick, chronically and systemically ill, through the use of root canals to save teeth and introduction of mercury amalgams to fill them.

Mercury was another interesting chapter in the history of dentistry. In 1840 when the precursor organization to the American

Society of Dental Surgeons was formed, members had to sign pledges that they would *not* use mercury in the fillings of teeth because of its potential for harm. A competing organization, the American Dental Association, was created and its leaders did not oppose the use of mercury. The battles fought over mercury amalgam in fillings, battles fought between the American Society of Dental Surgeons and the American Dental Association, were not unlike the violent disagreement between homeopaths and the American Medical Association. By the end of the nineteenth century the AMA and ADA had won both their wars.

In the 1920s a German chemist had revisited the problem of mercury amalgams. His thesis was that mercury from fillings was causing or stimulating many diseases. He gained much attention in Europe for his careful and methodical research and became the focus of attacks by the dental community. But when his laboratory and records were destroyed during World War II he lapsed into obscurity. Following the war, Dr. Reinhard Voll, again, was on the cutting edge of proving that mercury in the mouth was a poison to the system and possibly responsible for CFS, coronary artery disease, depression, and headaches.

Currently, according to the information given to me by Dr. Lee, many dentists, led by Dr. Hal Huggins of Colorado Springs, Colorado, believe there is a direct link between amalgam fillings and chronic illness. The American Dental Association, in retort, says, "Based on available scientific data the ADA has determined that the removal of amalgam restorations for the alleged purpose of removing toxic substances from the body, when such treatment is performed at the recommendation of the dentist, presents a question of fraud or quackery in all but an exceedingly limited spectrum of cases." Yet the Swedish government warns against using amalgam in the mouths of pregnant women and is considering a ban on the substances.

At the end of three hours of reading claims and counterclaims I was suddenly angry that science, so-called, couldn't get its act together. I was angry too to find myself in Phoenix, Arizona, paying big bucks to one dentist to repair a problem caused, it seemed, by dentistry. According to Dr. Meinig, extraction seemed to be the only solution to a root canal if it appeared that the person's immune system could not tolerate it. We had extracted the root canals, based on Linda's own diagnosis and Dr. Jordan's encouragement.

The problem still had not been resolved. Why? The root canal had not been extracted properly. The bone had not healed completely leaving small pockets (cavitations) in the bone. These cavitations became a home for toxins and infections. Dr. Meinig outlines a very specific protocol for removing a root-canaled tooth. This involves grinding out the periodontal ligament and the first millimeter of bone and flushing out the socket with a saline solution. This had apparently not been done when Linda's root-canaled molars had been pulled. The periodontal ligament which normally holds the root of the tooth to its bony socket does not break down during healing. As the bone heals and fills in, small spaces are left which become filled with necrotic tissue and infection. The surgical removal of this tissue and periodontal ligament was the procedure Linda was undergoing while I studied dentistry.

It was dark in the waiting room of the Camelback Dental Clinic. Suddenly, however, the light came on for me. The medical establishment, dentists included, were apparently hazardous to our health. Linda had originally been made ill by root canals. Her condition had been exacerbated by multiple visits to doctors and dentists who 1) extracted the root canals incompletely, leaving pockets of infection in her jaw and 2) prescribed many courses of antibiotics and steroidal drugs which stripped her body of healthy bacteria, allowing harmful bacteria to overwhelm her body's ability to fight infection, toxins and environmental poisons. They compounded the problem by not having the ability to diagnose specific causes, leaving us wandering aimlessly through their obstacle course.

After three hours, I asked how Linda was doing and the nurse invited me back. They were finishing up. Dr. Lee was a tall, serious man about my age. He explained that he had cavitated the three molars on the upper left side of Linda's jaw. Doug had diagnosed two but Dr. Lee believed a third area was also involved. He was excited about his work and told me of a seminar he had just attended involving blood studies.

"At the seminar I just attended," he whispered, "they were putting great stress on the healthfulness of a vegetarian diet. I'm not a vegetarian myself, but it is something to consider. "

"We've been vegetarians for over twenty years," I told him.

"The Germans are years ahead of us," he continued. "They've

developed so many excellent procedures and homeopathic medicines."

Linda was worn out. Her jaw was packed with gauze. She was trying to sit up.

"I think we got it all," said Dr. Lee. "It was a mess. Lots of cavities and tunnels. Really ugly stuff."

"It smelled pretty bad," said Baxann, Dr. Lee's assistant.

"We like to get a biopsy, just to be safe. It costs $100 but it's a good idea. By the looks of the material, I don't think it was cancerous."

"I don't think so either," said Baxann.

We were instructed to keep the packing on the stitches until the drainage stopped, given a packet of calcium, some Traumheel—a homeopathic medicine to aid healing—and something German, "Homeopathisches Arzneimittel," described as homeopathic penicillin. Dr. Lee said it was excellent.

I paid the bill. It was $1,200. They accepted my out-of-state check. Linda wanted an ice cream cone because she had been so good. We found a Baskin and Robbins on Camelback Boulevard and she ordered mint chocolate chip.

When we arrived at her mom and dad's, Linda took to her bed. The wound was draining. She thought it was bleeding and chomped on gauze and tea bags until the gum became, I thought, infected. A couple days after the surgery, I called Dr. Lee who advised us to report back for an inspection. We did. The incision was infected. Dr. Lee began treating the infection with injections of the homeopathic penicillin. We had to come back four times, every third day or so, for this treatment. The treatment, though painful, worked; the infection went away and Dr. Lee cleared Linda for travel.

Before we had returned to Dr. Lee for the gum infection, Linda experienced a classic natural healing event. It had been our mistake to not let the cavitations drain thoroughly after surgery. As a result, toxins were still held in the jaw area. Linda had been extremely uncomfortable and her right index finger began to hurt. The skin began to redden and swell at the first joint. A blister began to appear, then to enlarge. I lanced it with a needle and a huge amount of pus drained from the joint of the finger, demonstrating that the body does attempt to move poisons as far away from the vital organs as possible.

We thanked Dr. Lee for his help and I raised the possibility of removing Linda's amalgam fillings. Dr. Lee gave us reference material to read and suggested it was a decision he could not make for us. He was whispering again, a clear indication that the ground was not completely safe. The good doctor did provide Linda with a prescription for "Clifford Materials Reactivity Testing," a blood test which could predict patient sensitivity to various substances used in dental materials.

When we arrived home there was a package of remedies from Doug Leber and a biopsy from the Robert C. Bird Health Science Center at West Virginia University. The diagnoses per the biopsy was: "Chronic osteonecrosis and chronic fibrosing osteomyelitis (consistent with NICO: neuralgia-inducing cavitational osteonecrosis), maxillary left second and third molar area." According to the biopsy there was no evidence of malignancy.

The biopsy completely confirmed Doug Leber's EAV diagnosis. More important—the swelling around Linda's left eye, which had diminished slightly following Doug's initial treatments, entirely disappeared within two weeks following the cavitation surgery.

Chapter 18
Radionics

Linda began her course of Leber's homeopathic and herbal remedies. He gave her Amoebatox to kill off the amoebic parasites (giardia and E. histolytica), homeopathic phenylanaline for chest congestion, pain, and headache, Occuloplex I to relieve swelling eyelids, Hepatox to clean up the liver, and Geopathic Stress to alleviate nervousness, anxiety, and restlessness. These medicines, of course, caused Herxheimer-type reactions but Linda didn't miss a dose. She was determined to follow Leber's prescription. All were combination remedies produced by BioActive Nutritional of Melbourne, Florida.

My brother Bart invited us to house-sit for three weeks in March. Linda was up for it. A good sign. She believed the warm weather and salt water would be healing. We made preparations for Hawaii. We each bought a new bathing suit.

I hand-carried her little cardboard box of remedies through airport security to protect them from X-rays. We flew to San Francisco and got seats by ourselves on a DC-10 to Honolulu. It was the first week of March. Linda was feeling energetic for the first time in a year and a half. Our Honolulu arrival routine had been fixed over several visits. We collected luggage and took a cab to Bart's office in the Piikoi Building behind the Ala Moana Shopping Center. We toted our stuff onto the elevator and piled into the waiting room, arriving just at the end of office hours. Dr. Bart gave us adjustments and put us on a table for fifteen minutes of vibration and stretching which took the edge off the plane trip; then he drove us up the Pali Highway to a residential neighborhood to a large old Hawaiian house where the Hare Krishnas served a delicious vegetarian buffet.

We had come a long way from the time when chiropractic had been our only alternative to mainstream medicine. Many people had a great fear of chiropractic. The popping noises in their neck or back created by an adjustment generated phobic reactions. Bart used an Activator™ in his work. The Activator™ is a hand-held device with a spring-activated plunger. He placed the rubber tip of the small instrument on the vertebra and depressed a trigger. A nearly imperceptible but forceful movement of the rubber tip painlessly moved the vertebra. As a result, Bart had many patients who were not up to handling full spine manipulations.

I had my first adjustment when Bart was a student at Life Chiropractic college in Marietta, Georgia. I had been on a business trip to Georgia and spent a weekend with him. On Sunday afternoon we went to a small lake where his classmates were having a picnic. He was a first-year student and I had not been willing to let him practice on me. I was, frankly, concerned about paralysis. It seemed to me that if one's neck were jerked violently, the spinal column could be severed.

We swam out to a raft in the lake which was swarming with chiropractic students. I expressed my fears. They all laughed. "It can't hurt you," said a young woman in a pink bikini. She gave me an adjustment right there on the raft. For many years following I had monthly chiropractic adjustments, but never again under such delightful circumstances. I've had adjustments from a half dozen different chiropractic doctors. Some of these chiropractors believed the chiropractic was a panacea which could cure nearly any ailment. Their theory was that subluxations impede the nerves and thus the flow of energy to the various organs and systems of the body. By putting vertebrae back into alignment, the central, autonomic, and peripheral nervous systems can operate properly, insuring that the body functions properly.

More sophisticated chiropractors, like my brother, realize that the body is very complicated and that while eliminating misalignment of vertebrae is extremely helpful and can, in some instances, effect dramatic results, other important factors are nutrition, exercise, and emotional wellness. All chiropractors, however, practice natural or drugless medicine. Many can be criticized for their wham-bam approach. But, in that regard, they are no different from most medical doctors, who will keep you sitting alone in a cold little room in your underpants while they deal with the other four people who have the same appointment time.

Dr. Bart left for his holiday, and we began life, Hawaiian-style. The beach was across the street and we swam everyday—sometimes twice. It was idyllic except for the noise of automobiles, buses, trucks, and motorcycles making their way in a constant parade on Diamond Head Road. Linda was eager to swim and was clearly mending.

Bart had set her up with various people in his clinic for acupuncture, massage, and polarity therapy. Linda, however, wanted to see Sabrina Stevens, whom Bart had introduced us to in previous trips to Honolulu. Sabrina's office was a couple floors above Bart's in the Piikoi Building. Her business was called Kino Nani, "body beautiful" in Hawaiian. She was born and raised in Hawaii, daughter of a medical doctor. It is very difficult to describe what Sabrina does. It's easier to tell what happened to Sabrina and what she did about it.

When Sabrina Stevens was twenty-eight years old she was sleeping in her parent's home on the beach at Black Point. The homes along the beach are easily accessible. A crazed young man crept into the dark house and in the kitchen picked up a vegetable cleaver. In a scene like a bad horror movie, Sabrina awoke to see this "attractive, innocent-looking man" holding the cleaver above his head. She could smell glue or paint. He struck her four times on the face before she could raise her arm in defense. When he struck again the knife broke on two of her fingers and the man ran from the house. He was never apprehended, and Sabrina has never seen him again. In that violent moment he severely damaged two of her fingers and left four deep slashes on her face: on her forehead, her nose, eyelid, and down the side of her left eye.

Surgeons repaired the damage as best they could. The nerves were intact but because of trauma to her facial muscles Sabrina's face became distorted and lopsided. With the help of her family dentist, a specialist in cosmetic surgery, and using her own background in massage therapy, she began a research program to learn how to rehabilitate or resculpt her face. Sabrina was her own great experiment. She is, of course, her own best advertisement of the success of her technique. All one can see now (and you must look closely) is a faint scar running down the side of her left eye.

Linda was concerned that her jawbone and eye were not healing fast enough and that there might be damage to the tissue on the left side of her face. She thought Sabrina's facial sculpting and electrotherapy would be a possible solution to rebuilding that tissue and the facial muscles. And it turned out to be very helpful. During our time in Hawaii she had several sessions with Sabrina and was pleased with the results. Sabrina used electricity to stimulate the tissue of Linda's gums and jaw. She put on latex gloves and used her fingers inside Linda's mouth to massage the same area. The massage continued on the face around the eye and cheekbone. I dropped Linda off for the first of several appointments with Sabrina and headed to the local esoteric bookstore to search out material on another method of healing which I found fascinating in concept—radionics.

Reading about dowsing had led me to the subject of medical radiesthesia. Radiesthesia means sensitivity to radiations. I found a book by Abbe Mermet, a French priest, famous for locating water and missing persons, who operated on the following broad hypotheses:

"1. All bodies without exception are constantly emitting. . .radiations.

"2. The human body enters these fields of influence and becomes the seat of nervous reactions, of some kind of current which flows through the hands.

"3. If an appropriate object, such as a rod or a pendulum, is held in the hand, the invisible flux is made manifest in the movements given to this object, which acts as a kind of indicator."

In Europe, particularly in France, the radiesthesist is widely accepted. Medical dowsing or radiesthesia, then, is using a pendulum to discern radiations from the human body. Practitioners of radiesthesia have discovered that each person and each organ of the body give off measurable radiations. A sensitive operator of a pendulum can detect these radiations (in the same way that T.C. Lethbridge could discriminate gold from silver) and compare them against a norm. Thus, a medical radiesthesist could and does use a pendulum to diagnose medical problems. Furthermore, in the same way that Mr. Mechem could dowse for geopathic stress at a distance, a medical radiesthesist can diagnose and—hold onto your hat—even treat ailments at a distance.

Radionics, then, is the practice of diagnosing and treating health problems at a distance. A radionic practitioner can and does diagnose and cure ailments of people he or she has not personally met. On the face of it, this seems quite preposterous. But, on the face of it, finding water with a forked stick is likewise preposterous. There is a kind of telepathy involved with both radionics and water dowsing, and if one accepts either the belief must be based on an acceptance of Abbe Mermet's fundamental hypothesis.

Radionics, as a concept, is a mind boggler and as far afield from mainstream medicine as one can get. Skeptics might view radionics as voodoo at best but more likely as a complete figment of the imagination of those many people who practice radionics and receive radionic treatments. Yet, I have discovered, ex post facto, that the healing adventures of many chronically ill people have led them, inevitably, to a radionic practitioner when no one else could help them.

I obtained the name of a radionics practitioner through Bart, of course. (I was later surprised to find that there was a radionics practitioner in the Ashland area and that we had close friends, in Yakima of all places, who had experience with radionics practitioners located in Washington.) He asked around and discovered he had several close friends who were being treated by an individual in a western U.S. city. They were enthusiastic about his prowess as a healer, one claiming that she had "raised her kids with him." Another told me that when anyone in the family was ill, they simply picked up the phone and called "Jack" and he took care of it. Each cautioned me that Jack had to be protected from the FDA and medical community, who had a history of making life difficult for radionics and other alternative medicine practitioners. It was only because I was Bart's brother that they were willing to give me his number. The authorities had actually imprisoned people for practicing with the "black box." This all sounded quite dramatic and I promised to be discreet.

Hawaii with its warm salt water and soft winds was a healing experience. We didn't really want to leave the ocean view and unlimited supply of fresh papayas.

When we did finally return home, I called Jack and spoke to his answering machine. I had decided, based on my study of several books on radionics, that this was the kind of health treatment I wanted for myself and resolved that I, as well as Linda, would become his patient. A week or so elapsed before he called me back. When he did I explained which of his clients had referred me and that Linda and I both wished to be treated. Jack gave me a brief exposition on his practice of radionics. I asked if it were really illegal, and he told me that to diagnose and prescribe without a medical license was illegal. Use of radionic equipment, per se, was not. He did not diagnose or prescribe. But he was very confident of his ability to help. He explained that his was a twelve-month program, that it would take several months of treatment to clear infection, toxins, and inflammation from the system and a full year for the body to adjust to these changes. I asked him how frequent the treatments were. He answered that they were twenty-four hours a day.

"I would like you to call once a week and leave a brief message on my machine. I get forty to fifty calls a day so I can't possibly take them all. But I will get your message and I will act on it," said Jack in a crisp, almost official manner. He was articulate and professional, as brisk and quick as any medical doctor(s), whom he lumped with the pharmaceutical industry and FDA into the category "criminal conspiracy." I was a bit surprised by the brusqueness of his speech but liked his confidence; and since I, too, had begun to think of the medical/pharmaceutical industry as tainted, if not criminal, I found I was essentially in agreement with him. Besides, the price was right. Jack proposed to charge only $300 each to treat us radionically for the next year. I was shocked at the reasonableness of this low fee. I had expected a much, much higher price tag for a service which seemed too good to be true. Call in one's ailments by phone once a week and be healed!

Of course, it was a bit detached—impersonal, if you will. One would have to forego the charming bedside manner, the smile, the pat on the back, the intense personal attention one relies on from one's personal physician. It was a simple as ordering a shirt from a catalog. I sent Jack a check for $600 and a photo of each of us.

Radionic practitioners use what is called a "witness" to "make contact" with their clients. A witness is like an antenna. It can be a spot of blood, a teardrop, a lock of hair, some spit, a drop of urine, or a photo. According to radionic theory, a witness is imbued with the same radiational qualities as its source. It is not static or a snapshot in time. A witness will reflect the current condition of the subject in question. Thus, Jack claimed that he could use our photos (the ones I sent him were three years old) to assess our current state of health.

"Should I give you a rundown on our medical history?" I asked him.

"Don't bother," replied Jack. "I can figure it out."

The treatment, I presumed, began immediately. It was mid-May.

Jack had explained that he preferred to spend a couple of hours in person with his clients at the outset of treatment to explain his theories in detail and to describe his modus operandi. Since we lived some distance from him he waived this requirement, but encouraged us to come visit when we were able. In the meantime I began to give weekly phone updates. It was two months before we were able to arrange a visit. During that period I found it very difficult to wake up in the morning. And, occasionally, I could sense what felt like a buzzing in my chest. Linda had the normal aches and pains and was still taking Leber's medicines, plus a variety of flower essences. She was, however, making steady progress and was gaining strength. So many healing arts were involved with her turnabout that it was difficult, at that point, to give any credit to radionics.

I was a purer subject. I felt I was in good health and was looking forward to feeling better and was willing to give Jack the year he asked for.

Two months later, when we finally had the opportunity to visit Jack, we were surprised to find ourselves in a cul de sac of brick-veneered ranch-style dwellings built in the 1950s. Campers and boats were stored beside several of the houses, and the driveways were littered with bicycles, Big Wheels, and basketball hoops, evidence of families with children. It was hot when we arrived, and as we got out of the car I could hear splashing and kids squealing. The front door was open and I knocked on the screen door, then hollered a tentative "hello."

I'm not sure what we expected—a mad scientist, perhaps; a quirky little man with uncombed hair. We were certainly ready for something odd. Radionics, after all, was relegated to the dark underworld of alternative medicine. One might expect its practitioners to make a more interesting presentation than to locate themselves in a ranch-style house on a cul de sac. No, we weren't expecting Jack Taylor who appeared at the door tanned and healthy, blondish hair and blue eyes, wearing running shorts, Reeboks, and a polo shirt. He opened the door and sort of pulled us in, hugging each of us as if he knew us well (which maybe he did) and small-talked us down the stairs to his finished basement and into a room which had no windows.

Jack sat at a desk to the left of the door and directed us to a nicely appointed couch. "I forgot something," he said. "Right back."

We sat on the couch and looked around the room. On Jack's desk was a "black box"—a radionics instrument. I had seen photos of them in the books on radionics I had purchased in Honolulu. Jack's machine was set on edge rather than flat on the table, so that it looked like an instrument panel of an airplane. It was covered with well-worn dials, switches, and lights. In the small work area in front of the radionics machine was a pad. I knew, again from my reading, that this was a "stick pad." It worked in the same way as a pendulum. The operator would turn dials on the box, attempting to tune into a patient's problem while, at the same time, rubbing his finger across the pad. When a dial was tuned properly the finger would experience an increase in friction on the pad—a stick. This would mean that the dial was set to the proper rate.

Above the black box, on shelves which wrapped two sides of the room, were smaller instruments stacked two deep. I counted ninety-eight of them. Cords dangled from the machines and they gave off an electrical hum. Attached to each of these was a clip and in each clip was a bundle of photographs—the witnesses. Each of these instruments had several dials with numbers from 0 to 10, and each was set with a different rate. These were broadcasting machines and, again, from my research, I knew these were broadcasting vibrational rates to the individuals whose photos were clipped to the instrument.

Below the shelves were bookcases filled from the floor five feet up with books on physiology, medicine, herbology, homeopathy, acupuncture, flower essence therapy, psychology, and other healing arts. There was not enough room on the shelves for Jack's entire library, and it continued onto the floor in three rows of stacks at least three feet high. On the top of the stacks closest to me I could see several of my favorites including Dr. Gerber's *Vibrational Medicine* and *Bio-Circuits* by Leslie Patten. There was also a copy of Dr. Becker's *Body Electric* which I had not read, but which Sabrina told us had become the bible for her practice of electro-therapy. Dr. Becker has run successful experiments using electricity to regenerate tissue. I could also spot Dr. Bach's *Heal Thyself* and several books about Nicola Tesla, the once-famous electrical genius who claimed he could transmit electricity through the earth or atmosphere without use of power lines. In short, it was a much larger version of the library I had collected during the previous two years and reinforced my view that we had been on the right path.

Jack returned wearing longer pants and carrying a tray with glasses of mineral water. He sat down at his desk and picked up a thick stack of charts and quickly found ours. I could see the charts from my position on the couch. They were filled with small, neat notations in a code or shorthand. There was no computer or filing cabinet, no fax machine—just the humming instruments and books and Jack at his stick pad.

The phone rang. After one ring the answering machine clicked on, "This is Jack," said the crisp, professional voice as Jack turned to reach for the volume control, "I can't come to the phone right now, but if you'll leave. . ." The recording faded out to be replaced by Jack's own professional tones.

"I've been doing this full time for fifteen years," he told us beginning a discourse which lasted for over two hours. "At one time I was very ill, much sicker than Linda ever was, and in my search for good health I was led, ultimately, to a medical doctor who practiced radionics in his back room. He had used it for fifty years and because of his success with me I pestered him until, finally, he condescended to teach me what he knew. I was a medical technician and had some background in the medical arts. When he died, I took over his radionics practice. He willed his equipment to me. The instruments you see around this room are more than sixty years old. They're all rebuilt. It's very difficult to find good instruments. There are over eighty manufacturers of radionics equipment in the world but, unfortunately, most of it is junk. These machines were built by an old chiropractor who was a colleague of Dr. Ruth Drown. Dr. Drown was a pioneer in the development of radionics. She practiced in Hollywood and continued in the work developed originally by Dr. Abrams of the Stanford Medical School in the early 1900s. But in the 1950s, the medical community was being threatened, and they sicked their FDA partners on to such people as Dr. Drown, who ended up in jail. Radionics went underground in the United States, and Great Britain took the lead in its practice. It's quite legal in Great Britain. The history of radionics is fascinating and is detailed in a book called *Report on Radionics* by a British journalist named Edward Russell. I would strongly recommend you read it if you have any interest in this subject, which obviously you must. It's quite a story of how the pioneers of radionics had so many successes in healing people and, you might be surprised to know, reducing the need for pesticides in crops. They were so successful that the pharmaceutical/petro-chemical industries squashed the efforts of scientists who were achieving amazing results.

"The English method of radionics is dominated by the Theoso-phists led by David Tansley who, by the way, is an American. Tansley and his followers believe that illness originates in the more subtle physical bodies, the astral and the causal. Their treatment is focused on the chakras, and they use color and homeopathy as their primary methods of treatment. Their view is that changes in the astral body will manifest on the physical plane. My own method is somewhat different. Disease, in my view, manifests on the physical plane and can be dealt with at that level. Because of my own personal spiritual beliefs, I don't feel it's proper for me to mess around with my client's astral bodies. It's not necessary. Over fifteen years I have proven to myself that excellent results can be achieved by directing my attention to the cellular level.

"Now it is important for you to understand that disease is cumulative. Throughout our lifetimes we are constantly exposed to viruses, bacteria, environmental toxins and chemical toxins, from pharmaceutical drugs. We are likewise exposed to a myriad of life conditions and situations: stress, exercise, nutrition, overwork, no exercise, bad air, contaminated water, etc. Our bodily systems, our immune systems fight to maintain some sort of equilibrium with the forces arrayed against it. For example, your intestinal tract contains three to four pounds of bacteria. In a healthy state there is a symbiosis but, for example, if one were to take several courses of antibiotics, the balance between good and bad bacteria in your system could weigh in the favor of the bad bacteria. Symptoms could begin to manifest and chronic illness result.

"You see, we all have accumulations of viruses, bacteria, and toxins. Processed food is loaded with harmful chemicals. Water is contaminated with bacteria, parasites, and heavy metals. Viruses and bacteria abound in the air. Our bodies, under normal conditions, are able to deal with moderate levels of all of these negative conditions. But, if the toxins reach a certain level, symptoms will develop. If nothing is done, chronic illness is the inevitable outcome.

"I think it is quite clear to the American public that this hypothesis is true. We know our air is polluted, our water contaminated, our food adulterated with chemicals. The problem is that the great mass of our citizens see no way out. They must put up with it and do the best they can and, most unfortunately, they are required to look to the medical establishment for assistance. This is the true horror story of our society, because our medical system is significantly adding to the damage by its pervasive and persuasive use of chemical therapy. Doctors are great when it comes to broken bones and suturing cuts, and there are situations where surgery and perhaps even drug intervention is called for, but medical doctors have no clear view of illness and disease and are so dominated by the pharmaceutical industry that 98 percent of the time their only recourse is to prescribe a chemical. This might give temporary relief, but in every case adds to the accumulation of poisons in the cellular body, thus diminishing the ability of the immune system to deal with virus, bacteria, and other harmful agents. The medical community is an epidemic. Their practice damages the health of our society. For most people there is no way out of the American medical loop. The typical American citizen is bound to the medical community by propaganda and by insurance. There is no alternative for the average citizen. People seek out alternatives only when they reach the end of their ropes—when chemistry has failed them completely. As a result, the alternative practitioners get the hard cases. And because we get cases of last resort it is easy for medical doctors to claim that we don't have much to offer. I've had many occasions when people have carried their dying relatives down the stairs to this room and laid them on the couch where you are sitting. They have been beaten and battered first by their family doctor and then an array of specialists, then doused with chemicals, irradiated, suffered invasive tests and surgeries to end up on a couch in the basement of my house with their sons and daughters, mothers and fathers saying, 'Jack, is there anything you can do?'"

Jack stopped to take a sip of water. I relaxed my fingers, for I had been feverishly taking notes. I glanced at Linda who was smiling, entranced. Linda made up her mind about people very quickly. She loved Jack; that was plain to see.

A young voice hollered "Dad, Dad!" and a husky twelve-year-old dripped down the steps in a wet surfer's bathing suit. "I stayed under two and a half minutes!" he hollered, then turned, not waiting for a comment and ran back up the stairs. I heard a yell and a splash.

"Nice-looking kid," I said.

"I've got two boys," Jack told us. "They're twelve and fourteen, and they've never seen a medical doctor except for a broken bone or two."

Although Jack had carried on about the medical community with a great deal of energy and obvious sincerity, he had relayed his views without a great deal of obvious emotion.

"Aren't you just a bit bitter?" I wanted to know. "Obviously, you feel you can be more helpful than medical doctors, yet you're down here in your basement sort of hiding out while the docs. . ."

"Are going to all-expenses-paid conventions at five-star resorts around the world, courtesy of pharmaceutical companies," he interrupted. "I don't think I'm embittered. I can't change the world. All I can do is assist a handful of people to get well. It's irritating, I will admit, to see the damage done to some of the folks I end up seeing in this room. And that's where I should make a correction in your comment. It's not that I am *more* helpful. I am helpful. Medical doctors are also victims of the system. Our so-called health care industry is making people sick. The medical establishment is, according to one of my most valuable books, a major threat to health."

He reached out and picked a hardcover book off one of the stacks. He held it up for us, his two newest students, to see: *Medical Nemesis: The Expropriation of Health,* by Ivan Illich. I dutifully made a note.

"It may be out of print for all I know," said Jack. "But it is brilliant. Well-argued and meticulously documented. Illich argues that all medical matters should be demystified and that lay people take control over medical perception, classification, and decision making." Illich says that it is a sick system and that medicine is not in a position to heal itself. There is a term which you have probably heard for physician-caused illnesses—'iatrogenic disease.' Medical journals themselves have documented that one out of every five patients admitted to a hospital acquires iatrogenic disease. One in thirty of these cases results in death. Half are caused by drug therapy. Now who in their right mind would check into a hospital if they knew they had a one-in-five chance of getting a medically-caused illness and a one-in-thirty chance of dying from that medically-caused disease? I don't know what kind of business you're in but with that kind of a record they'd sue you, close you down, or put you in jail.

"People, particularly younger people, are already suspicious of the drug industry and hospitals and doctors, but they don't have the scientific data necessary to confirm their beliefs."

"I guess that's why people spend billions of their own money every year on alternative health care," I quickly interjected.

"And that's why the AMA, FDA, and the pharmaceutical industry want to discredit and shut down alternative methods of care. They took out homeopathy at the turn of the century and have made a hard run at chiropractors in the last twenty years. Interestingly, the chiropractors won their case in court, and the AMA had to back off.

"But enough ranting and raving," said Jack. "Let me tell you how I operate. First of all, I'm glad you took the time to come visit with me because we won't have the opportunity to chat very often. You will communicate with me as you have been doing via the telephone answering machine, and I will respond appropriately. Initially, I'd like you to call me once a week and give me a brief recap of your condition." (I noted he was promising no treatment.) "Tell me good things as well as bad. As you begin to feel better, and you will feel better, your calls may be less frequent. If you become ill, call more frequently. I'll leave that up to you. Every couple of months remind me that it's time for a chat, and I'll call you and bring you up-to-date on what I've been doing.

"During the first four to five months of consultation I deal with everyone the same way unless there is an acute condition which needs to be resolved. What my predecessor discovered, and what I've confirmed, is that we are all suffering from an accumulation of the same forty to fifty viruses, bacteria, and toxins. So, in that four-to-five month period I will clear forty to fifty of these accumulations from your system. Actually, I've done quite a bit with you two already but I'll get to that in a minute. After this four to five months we will have eliminated 80 to 90 percent of your problems, and then we can whittle away at anything which still troubles you. Your body will need to make adjustments to these changes, and if you are familiar at all with the concept of the healing crisis, then you won't be surprised when I tell you to expect some bad days as these infections are dissolved out of your system. What will have more impact, however, are the feelings of wellness which will sweep through you with increasing frequency."

Linda interrupted Jack and relayed her experiences with die-off reaction from candida, the abscess on her finger after dental surgery, and the many skin ailments she had experienced over the previous nineteen months.

"Many of the so-called symptoms you experienced such as coughing, sneezing, watery eyes, fever, flatulence, indigestion, nausea, headaches, sinus drainage, and the like can be viewed as the body's attempt to discharge the accumulation of old infections and toxins from your body. Western medicine, for example, postulates that viruses cause flu and colds, and they have, in fact, identified nearly 200 different viruses which could be involved. Chinese medicine, on the other hand, suggests that colds and flu are positive. They are a healthy elimination process in which viruses participate. They don't cause the flu or the cold. They exacerbate, aggravate, and possibly even initiate this elimination process. Every human has had their entire lifetime, beginning with conception, to accumulate poisons in their system. This infection and toxicity begins during fetal development. Infections, toxins, poisons, chemicals, and environmental toxic materials permeate our tissues. If these reach the chronic or symptomatic level and if no healing is taking place, the cumulative gunk remains, regenerating additional endotoxins (the waste product of viruses and bacteria) and, ultimately, causing damage to cells, tissues, glands, and organs."

Jack paused to take a deep breath, then continued. "The good news is that our bodies have amazing regenerative abilities when we give them opportunity to heal. Blood plasma regenerates in about 10 days, white cells in 30 to 80 days, most soft tissues in 90 days, and red blood cells in 120. Each cell and tissue in the body regenerates every seven years. The gunk, unfortunately, remains, accumulating and, if not dealt with, causing degenerative disease processes of all types.

"Getting well is serious business, and it is only logical to assume that it can take some time. If chronic disease is the result of a lifetime of cellular accumulations, then it is unreasonable to expect that a pill or a surgery can clean up the system overnight. What is required is a program. We need to neutralize the infections, toxins, and inflammations in the system, eliminate them through the bowel, urinary tract, the skin, nose, mouth, ears, and eyes, while at the same time providing our bodies with proper nutrition, rest, air, sun, and exercise. My job is to assist in neutralizing the infections and inflammation using radionics. Your responsibility is to rebuild your cellular structure by eating and living as healthily as you can. Before you go I'll give you some detailed information on diet."

"What type of diet do you recommend?" I quickly asked.

"Are you familiar with macrobiotics?" Jack wanted to know.

We were, of course, courtesy of Dr. Bart Smith. Several years previously, when he discovered that I could not prepare a meal, Bart insisted that I learn. He spent dinnertime for a week teaching me the basics of macrobiotic cookery which required that I buy a pressure cooker, wok, suribachi, pickle press, brown rice, sea salt, tamari, miso, squash, sauerkraut, daikon radish and ginger root, tofu, seitan, ume plums, and seaweeds—and eschew dairy products, sugar, and the horrible nightshade family (tomatoes, eggplant, and potatoes). I became much enamored with macrobiotics—enjoyed it, in fact, loved the smell of roasted sesame seeds and the grinding of sea salt but, frankly, found it difficult to avoid tomatoes and all dairy. We had never become 100 percent macrobiotic, but it strongly influenced our diet and was a significant influence in what we ate. Thus, we were not surprised or put off by Jack's suggestion.

"I'll give you some material on macrobiotics. I know you are vegetarians; I am too. Macrobiotics is not strictly vegetarian, as it allows certain types of fish. You can leave out the fish, of course. Macrobiotics has a tendency towards being a bit fanatical. So, don't go overboard. Just try to stick to the basics; eat locally grown organic whole grains and vegetables when possible. Also, it's time for you to give up the "lacto" in your lacto-vegetarian diet. I strongly suggest you stop eating cheese, butter, ice cream, or milk. It is fattening and carries germs—within an hour of a putting cube of butter on the kitchen table you will be able to find an accumulation of tuberculosis bacilli. Which brings me to my analysis of you two. Both of you showed a high level of tuberculosis when we started back in May. Don't worry; it's long gone. Randy, you especially, were high in tuberculosis. Were you experiencing any coughing or chest pain?"

I told him I was not, and Jack was surprised.

Jack then reviewed his findings for both of us. He looked at seven areas initially. In each area he had developed a point scale that measured the area against a norm or healthly status. On the first area, for example, which he called "nerve pressure," serious problems would develop at 3,400 to 4,000 points. Nerve pressure was caused by toxins exerting pressure on the brain and, in its most serious forms, manifested in symptoms of encephalitis, Lou Gehrig's disease, Parkinson's, epilepsy, multiple sclerosis, and 80 percent of the worst psychological diseases. As of May I had been at 2,244, with Linda slightly better at 2,145. Most adults, we learned, were over 1,800 but, according to Jack, we would finish the program after a year with nerve pressure under 300 points and would, as a result, notice that we were calm, relaxed, quiet.

"Red blood cells" was the second category which had its own scale. The score for red blood cells was an indicator to Jack of our ability to oxygenate, a measurement of the efficiency of our metabolism. Again, Linda's score was slightly better than mine.

The third test was "white blood cells," which measured the overall level of infection. The higher the count, the higher the infection. Linda, once again, was better. According to Jack, both of our scores indicated to him that we had moderate levels of chronic cumulative infection.

The fourth test was for "vitality." Vitality measured the overall strength of the immune system. Linda was better!

"Toxicity," test number five, was an indicator of the accumulation of chemicals in our tissues. Linda had a slightly better score.

Test number six was "inflammation." Linda was over two hundred points better than I was.

The seventh and last category was "primary infections." Again, Jack reiterated, every human has an accumulation of infections. His scale was:

    60 to 90 points—nonsymptomatic
    90 to 200 points—clear symptoms
    200 to 300 points—very symptomatic
    300 to 400 points—serious
    400+ points—critical

We had shown higher than average levels of strep, staph, and E. coli. Our most serious infection had been tuberculosis. I say "had been" because Jack assured us these infections had been neutralized since shortly after he had started with us on May 18. My TB score had been 216, and Jack had been shocked when I claimed no symptoms. He told us that TB was virulent in the United States and was a primary cause of allergic reactions. TB could also cause encephalitis and arthritis. In our systems, we were pleased to hear, he had found no cysts or precancerous conditions and no parasites.

I realized I was feeling a bit sulky. What Jack was telling me through his scoring system was that even two months ago, Linda had been healthier than I.

Jack's analysis indicated that I was the sicker one! How could this be? I considered myself to be a healthy person. And, I'd been her nursemaid for the last year and a half. What the hell was going on with this radionics stuff?

"All these numbers are very confusing," I told Jack. They make it sound like I'm the sick one. How can this be?"

"Again," replied Jack, "I need to have you think in terms of disease as a process of accumulation. It takes place over time, like the pollution of a body of water, and the outward manifestation of this pollution is affected by many other factors.

"In your case, for example, you didn't get many doses of antibiotics over a year's time. You may have been in better physical condition. Your constitution might be stronger. You may have the inherent ability to withstand higher levels of poisoning. Each person is unique. We don't always react in the same way at the same time. However, at some point in the future, these accumulations would have begun to cause you some difficulty.

"I know I've told you that chronic disease is a cumulative process twenty times in the last hour. I can't harp on it enough. It doesn't just drop in. It may be brought by the gods but their method of bringing it to you is the drip method. I'm not saying you were unhealthy. I'm just saying you are no different from any other citizen of this world. The fact of our life on this planet is that we are subjected to a plethora of agents which can cause harm over time. The good news is that these agents, for the most part, can be neutralized using vibrational therapy. These machines you see around the room broadcast very specific vibrational rates to the individuals whose photos are attached. These rates are picked to counter the vibrational rates of, for example, E. coli. The broadcast or healing rate will meet the E. coli rate and liquefy it, that is, dissolve it in the cell. To make a gross oversimplification, it works like the crystal glass in the TV commercial. When a singer hits and holds a note vibrating at the proper rate, the glass dissolves. Again, to keep it simple, that's how radionics works. We identify the vibrational rate of the "problem" and broadcast an equal but opposite rate which destroys the virus, bacteria, or toxin.

"Radionics does have limitations. If there has been degenerative damage to tissue, nerve covering, or bony structure, radionics can't put it back. However, in many cases (back injuries for example), pain can be relieved by eliminating inflammation and infection. Many subluxations of the spine are caused by inflammation and infection—chiropractors can adjust you repeatedly, and, the treatments have no effect because the inflammation and infection remain."

"How often will you treat us?" Linda wanted to know.

"I'll be broadcasting selected rates to you for twenty-four hours a day until your numbers reach a normal range," said Jack.

"I don't quite understand how you know what rate to use," said Linda.

"Each person, each toxin, each organ, each specific condition of the body has a unique vibrational rate. The Law of Interference says that when frequencies which are 180 degrees opposite meet, they neutralize each other. This is what happens when we broadcast radionic rates. First, the primary infections break down into a liquid state in the system, allowing blood and lymph to pull them out. This allows the body to eliminate cell and tissue damage by throwing off dead cellular debris. At the same time, the by-products of infection, endotoxins and ectotoxins (the eliminative wastes of microorganisms), are neutralized and pulled out and removed to the kidneys, liver, bowel, urinary tract, mucous membranes, and skin for purging. Radionics can't affect structure. By that, I mean conditions like kidney stones, gall stones, nerve damage, or degeneration of bone. Those are problems for the surgeons. But often, radionics can bring some relief by knocking out related infection and reducing inflammation."

Jack then took a new photo of us sitting on the couch together and retested us by having us each, in turn, hold onto a copper wire connected to the machine. In just two months we had both showed significant improvement. This, of course, was easy for Jack to say and impossible for us to verify except subjectively by how we felt. I was still disturbed that my May scores had shown me to be in worse shape than Linda. Yet, at this point there seemed to be no risk involved. If radionics didn't do anything, we weren't out that much money. Maybe I was sicker than she was right now. I was past fifty and, until my session with Jack, still feeling bulletproof. Maybe I shouldn't even be thinking in terms of "sicker." It was only a measurement of my accumulations, after all.

Jack asked Linda if anything was currently bothering her. For the previous two days she had been experiencing a severe pain in her cheekbone and eye. This recurrence of the eye pain, without any swelling, had created much anxiety. She was very concerned that the jaw infection was coming back. Jack rubbed his stick pad and turned dials on the instrument. It took five minutes or so until he said, "It's just a secondary virus. These bugs may plague you intermittently in the weak areas of your tissues. Don't worry though. This one will be gone in an hour." The way he said it, I believed him. It was a guarantee.

We stood to leave, smiling all around, slightly exhausted from trying to collate all the information Jack had attempted to impart. He gave us copies of articles on macrobiotics, avoidance of dairy foods, and a seaweed-based liquid vitamin supplement which he strongly recommended. "Keep in touch," he told us, closing the screen door.

We drove up the busy freeway in rush-hour traffic, heading for home. An hour later I asked Linda about the pain in her eye. "Completely, totally gone," she told me.

Chapter 19
Spider's Song

Sitting on the front porch, hidden by a stone pillar, I watched Linda climb the steep hill to our house. She was wearing a day pack loaded with groceries for lunch and dinner. The cats, sensing or hearing her steps on the hill, ran down to meet her, making their odd greeting noises. She was smiling, of course, now chronically happy, reborn, possessing a newer, cleaner body, a refreshed spirit and thick new hair. Linda stopped, bent down and picked up her old calico cat. They were simpatico. Kitty had survived a serious winter illness, and we had observed closely as she fasted, slept in the meager winter sunlight, ate what grass she could find, purged it and sipped water, finally becoming well, using some kind of natural cat-healing techniques.

Linda looked fit and beautiful. She had made the long climb from the bottom of the pond of unwellness like an ugly dragonfly nymph, emerging with bright shiny wings—the imago.

Watching her progress up the front walk, I was overcome by another attack of smugness. We had faced the unsolvable medical dilemma and had unraveled the mystery. Linda was well, better than ever. She was almost wacky on wellness. In the months after our meetings with Doug Leber, Dr. Lee, and Jack Taylor, as she grew stronger, Linda had experienced frequent bouts of anxiety—a fear of sliding back into the quicksand of illness. I would sharply tell her that it would not happen and even if it did, we now had a broad-based methodology for dealing with disease. I called Jack once a week as he had instructed. I had few complaints to report. Linda had several serious headaches. Each time I called and left a message about her headache, it would disappear in a few hours.

Radionics certainly could not replace all modalities of treatment. Jack, for example, didn't answer his phone on the weekends, and a couple of times during the year he would be gone for a week or more. But we developed a high degree of confidence in his ability to help us. We could visualize healing radiations filling our house, attacking those bacteria and viruses, loosening the sordid accumulations which clogged our fifty-year-old cells, dissolving the poisons and flushing them through our elimination systems, cleansing our tissues from inside out. We were pleased with radionics.

I was confident that we had developed insights that would guarantee our wellness. As we no longer had medical insurance of any kind, it was important that we stay healthy.

My wife had become seriously ill. No conventional medical practitioner was able to diagnose Linda's ailment or prescribe a cure. For over a year we operated within the system. Thirteen establishment doctors (two emergency room specialists, a general practitioner, two ophthalmologists, an ear-nose-throat specialist, an allergist, a radiologist, an internist, a dermatologist, a preventive medicine specialist, a dentist, and an oral surgeon), using blood tests, CAT scans, X-rays, and their collective diagnostic skills could not tell us what to do or where to go. Most, however, felt free to prescribe a course of antibiotic or steroidal chemicals, hoping to stop her ever-growing list of symptoms.

Serendipitously, guides began to appear. We experienced the reality of psychic knowledge as practiced by dowsers. My dying wife and I suspended disbelief and began a journey into the underworld of healing therapies. We left the secure world of conventional medicine and walked a tightrope without the safety net of medical insurance.

Our attitude toward medical insurance was evidence of the dramatic change in our thought process which had evolved over the previous two-and-one-half years. We had applied for a medical insurance plan, but whatever the doctors reported to the underwriters caused them to decline Linda for coverage. Ironically, at a point in her life when she was the most healthy, the infinitely wise insurance industry deemed her unfit—an unacceptable risk. She was apprehensive at first about the lack of coverage. We discussed it and realized that with the exception of emergency treatment for accidental injuries, broken bones, cuts, and gunshot wounds, there was not much that hospital-based medicine had for sale that we wished to purchase. We didn't want to buy drugs, being drug free. We didn't want a hysterectomy, or a heart bypass or an organ transplant. We didn't want radiation or chemotherapy. We no longer accepted the concept that traditional medical merchandise and service were all there was available in the marketplace. We had found other sources of medical help. It's a long journey from antibiotics to radionics. We had taken the trip and survived. Not only survived, but thrived.

Granted, we enjoyed several advantages over many people who had to deal with chronic illness. I could afford to spend full time attacking the problem, and we had saved some money which enabled us to chase solutions from one end of the West Coast to the other.

But most importantly, and to our credit, we had taken responsibility. Maintaining our health was our job, not the job of a doctor—medical, naturopathic, or "other." We had decided that responsibility for our wellness could not be delegated. We had to develop a program based on our new information sources to keep us healthy. We had to be our own personal trainers, recognizing that right action in our fifties might make our sixties, seventies, and eighties tolerable, enjoyable, even exciting.

At fifty-two I was feeling better and stronger than at any time of my life. Energy was something I'd lost track of over the years. Lack of energy, burnout, if you will, had turned me from an insurance-peddling, Kiwanis-attending, country club-belonging, small-town American into a premature retiree. Now I was saying things like, "I haven't had this much energy since I was a kid." I had difficulty staying in bed in the morning. I would wake up, make lists of thing to do, then actually do them. Energy allowed me to do more.

Most mornings I would begin with Qigong, and though I suspected I was a slow student in the esoteric aspects of feeling the movement of the energy, the exercise over a period of two years of practice had changed my body. I was limber, flexible, loose, balanced, and coordinated.

Our eating habits improved as we ate more macrobiotically and, for the most part, bought organic grains, fruits, and vegetables. We did a good job of eliminating most dairy and sugar from our diet. We supplemented our food with the seaweed-based vitamin and mineral drink called "Body Balance" made by Life Force, Inc., which Jack Taylor had recommended, took extra vitamin C and (I hesitate to say it) yet one more multilevel marketed herbal supplement called "Plus" that we got through the Mannatech Company. The Mannatech sales force made all sorts of testimonials that were annoying. But Plus did level blood sugar drops, which had always made me obnoxious when I got hungry. Another of their supplements—MVP—seemed to be an energy booster. We were doing so many different things that it was difficult to point to any one and make claims about its efficacy. We were still not scientists. Anecdotally, though, our total program was working.

Our first-aid kit had changed dramatically. It was no longer aspirin, Vicks, and mercurochrome. On hand was Rescue Remedy for emotional upsets, Traumheel for minor injuries, tea tree oil and lavender for cuts, nux vomita for nausea, goat whey and aloe vera juice for indigestion, apis for stings and bites, lobelia for chest congestion, kava kava and arnica for muscle soreness, biocircuits for headaches or sleeplessness. There were other products which we hadn't yet gotten around to experimenting with: colloidal silver, a natural antibiotic; Willard Water, which allegedly charges the body's electromagnetic system; and a remarkable ointment discovered in a peat bog in Wenatchee, Washington, by a friend of my dad. In addition, we had other tricks which I have not detailed for the reader: Transcend Cards with radionic rates imprinted on them which seem to relax and restore the body, an acupressure hook used to self-administer pressure point therapy and a cupboard full of flower essences, herbal tinctures, and homeopathic cell salts. Staying healthy was more fun when one operated under a suspension of disbelief.

We didn't need the first-aid kit too often. We felt too good; slept too well; defecated in championship style.

Our attitudes toward illness had changed completely. Gone was the medieval dread of mysterious diseases descending on us out of the night. Disease could, we believed, be prevented. There was, in fact, a preventive medicine, and it did not involve an annual physical with prostate palpitation, pap smear, and mammogram. Preventive medicine was tied to life-style, mind style, and environment. If we did become ill, we had access to more than one means of diagnosis.

By January of 1995 Linda could have been described as "well" by most people's definition. As Jack had promised the previous July, her sense of wellness had steadily increased; her long list of symptoms regularly diminished. With the exception of stiff fingers and a morning cough, she had regained the level of health and wellness she enjoyed prior to the "spider bite." (She still held to the spider bite theory; I accepted it as a useful metaphor.) She began to take over certain household chores. She could comfortably walk three miles, wanted to go out and invite people in.

Our friends Rick and Carlotta had consulted with Doug Leber after Linda's good experience and had also, coincidentally, gone through cavitation surgery. They convinced Doug to come to Ashland to see people who had expressed an interest in EAV analysis. Doug and his wife and youngest child spent three days at Rick and Carlotta's house. He rechecked Linda and found that her jaw infection was clear, and her liver problem was nearly resolved.

In the evening after Linda's second EAV, Doug gave an informal lecture to the people who were having the analysis and others who were interested. After reviewing his educational background, his first introduction to Dr. Voll's electroacupuncture theories, trips to Germany to study, and his own development of the Computron, Doug outlined his theory of wellness. Throughout his career, as the result of his experiments with the Computron, he had developed a list of factors which were obstacles to good health. This was a hierarchical list; it was critical that the problems at the top of the list be eliminated first. If they were not, it would be difficult to get well. The first ten items were:

1. Dysbiosis—This condition exists when the microflora of the body are out of balance. Consisting of bacteria, yeast, and fungi, the microflora coat the skin, mucous membranes, and genitourinary tract. When they are healthy the flora contain trillions of microbes which literally help the body fight off pathogenic organisms. Overuse of antibiotics produces an overgrowth of fungus such as C. albicans, which is involved in chronic illness. According to Doug, 60 percent of the general population and 80 percent of individuals with chronic health problems have dysbiosis.

2. Psychological Stress—Traumatic events, if unresolved, can be stored away, creating a stress condition which can adversely affect the endocrine system and setting health problems in motion which may not show up until years later. 60 percent of the general population have psychological stress including a very high percentage of the chronically ill.

3. <u>Parasite Toxicity</u>—Healthy immune systems can tolerate parasites. These organisms convince your body to let them live off your blood and tissue and handle their waste products (excretions). These organisms can actually secrete chemicals which cause cravings for food, e.g. sugar, which they want and need. Most are ingested through drinking water but also come from meat or animals (pets). Although hydrochloric acid in the stomach will get rid of them under healthy conditions, they are usually the hardest problem to resolve when they gain a foothold. When present, parasites can actually accelerate the growth of cancerous tumors. Eighty percent of the population has one or more parasites. Ninety-five percent of patients with chronic illness will have them.

4. <u>Mouth Currents</u>—When there are two dissimilar metals in the mouth such as exist in amalgam fillings, crowns, and bridges, a battery effect occurs, using saliva as the solution to conduct electricity. This situation is present twenty-four hours a day and the current is measurable with proper instruments. A current of 3 microamps can be handled by the body but in some cases, 50 to 60 microamps is not unusual. Forty percent of the general population have this factor and 50 percent of the chronically ill have mouth currents.

5. <u>Geopathic Stress</u>—Disturbances created by electromagnetic force fields from the earth itself can be positive (charging—producing hypertension or insomnia) or negative (discharging—producing fatigue, weakness, cancer). When geopathic stress is present it blocks energetic therapies such as homeopathy from working. Seven percent of the population is affected, as are 35 percent of the chronically ill.

6. <u>Focal Toxicity</u>—These can be active infection, or toxins from an inactive infection, or an abscess. A concentration of toxins will lead to cysts, polyps, fatty tumors, or even allergic reactions or brain chemistry problems. Natural medicine can assist in reducing the foci but if they have progressed beyond a certain point, a surgical procedure may be required. Areas that can be affected include the appendix, teeth, tonsils,

sinuses, lymph tissues, bile ducts, fallopian tubes, eustachian tubes, tear ducts, retina, and spermatic cord.

7. Chemical Sensitivities/Allergies—Pollutants in air, water, food, solvents, chemicals, etc., need to be identified and neutralized.

8. Heavy-Metal Toxicity—Heavy-metal accumulations adversely affect the autonomic nervous system.

9. Mercury Poisoning—Twenty years after a mercury filling is put in, half of it will have dissolved as vapor. Mercury vaporizes at 98°. This situation is present twenty-four hours a day with no relief to the body. In patients who have excessive dental work, metal plating occurs, and black line or mercury tattoo can be seen on the gum as the ions are pulled into the tissue. When the mercury is dispersed, it will go to many areas of the body; no specific organ is affected. The problem may not be obvious but it is like having a seemingly clean house; then you sweep and have a pile of dirt on the floor.

10. Lack of Exercise—A sedentary lifestyle is an obstacle to health. A body overburdened with toxins and inactive is unlikely to throw them off. Exercise can flush out lots of poisons by causing the body to sweat and pumping blood and lymph through the body.

These were the top ten obstacles to healing the chronically ill. A pretty ugly picture—you probably have fungus; you're screwed up mentally; might have worms; your mouth could jump start a Volkswagen; you're infected, polluted, poisoned by your dentist and you don't get enough exercise. Other than that, you are doing fine! Get well soon.

It was important in Doug's philosophy to eliminate problems at the top of the list and then work down. The remaining obstacles were:

11. Scar Disturbance—which affected flow of ch'i through the meridians.

12. Electromagnetic Disturbance—caused by electric appliances, power lines, etc.

13. Food Allergies
14. Structural Imbalance
15. Root-Canaled Teeth
16. Nutritional Deficiency
17. Impure Drinking Water
18. Poor Food Combining
19. No Quiet Time
20. Overweight Condition
21. Smoking
22. Shallow Breathing
23. Overwork
24. Alcohol Problem
25. Improper Chewing
26. Inadequate Water Intake
27. Drug Problem
28. Radiation

Doug's view, as reflected in the notes I made from his comments, is that improving nutrition, quitting smoking, avoiding alcohol, drinking adequate amounts of pure water, combining food properly, and exercise could not alleviate chronic illness if, for example, one still had mercury poisoning, geopathic stress, or some other obstacle higher on the list. Doug Leber's list of obstacles to wellness was a more detailed recital of Jack Taylor's theory of disease being caused by accumulations of toxins, poisons, and infections.

Linda still had a few issues to deal with, and within a week another box full of herbal and homeopathic remedies arrived by UPS, designed, we presumed, to attack her remaining ailments. This time there was no healing crisis. We both believed that the long period of illness was over. We no longer thought much about it or talked much about it. Unwellness was not all-consuming.

After the lecture we drove home and took a long walk to clear our heads. I had trouble keeping up with Linda. When we got back to the house she announced that it was the first time in two years she had walked without pain.

LINDA'S VOICE: *I had a dream about Grandma last night. I was little, sitting on her lap in the kitchen of her old house. She has her arms around me. I'm all curled up and feel small but the odd thing is I'm the age I am now. I'm thinking, "This is wonderful."*

I feel so safe and calm. I look around—My mother is sitting across the table and someone else? Do they think I'm silly? I can't tell for sure. But it doesn't matter. I love being there. I want to stay in that kitchen—protected—in that house—looking out the window into the backyard—trees, flowers, windows, red and white.

As far as I was concerned, this particular healing adventure was over. Armed with new attitudes, we were ready for whatever the future might bring. Both of us were changed, physically and mentally. We had learned that there are no panaceas; no silver bullets; no one individual or book with all the answers. Health required a complete program which includes clean water, good air, nutritious whole foods, vitamin and mineral supplemention, exercise, a relaxed mind, self-discipline, and good luck. If we developed an illness, we had a whole list of new tools to fall back on. If a serious problem developed, we could call on Dr. Osterhaus, Doug, or Jack, or someone like them. We now were in a network that would allow us to become aware of other alternative therapies that might be evolving.

Sharing the adventure had brought Linda and me closer together. We were a better couple. We had found antidotes for our anecdotes, and I noted that we were less interested, less preoccupied with health issues now that Linda was well.

I was proud that we had found the answers to an illness which the conventional practitioners could not even diagnose. But we were not so arrogant as to think we did it by ourselves. Guides and books appeared in the most curious ways to lead us to the next level of understanding. We were thankful for the help we had received from Bart, Joyce, Henry, Fred, Renee, Mich, Meech, Doug, Sabrina, and Jack. Thankful also for Dr. Osterhaus, Dr. and Mrs. Turska, and Dr. Lee and Baxann. Grateful for the work of Dr. Bach, Dr. Hahnemann, Leon Eeman, Dr. Jensen, Dr. Voll, and Dr. Gerber. It was a great team of helpers, healers, and teachers. Curiously, much of what they taught us isn't all that new. Much of our exploration introduced us to technologies or practices which are prevalent in other counties and were, in some cases, well-known and widespread in the United States in years past.

I wished that more of the chronically ill could make contact with the people we had met. But I realize that time and culture are huge impediments to change. People have to keep slugging it out. One doesn't have time to get well. And it's hard to give up a medical system which is all-pervasive.

We ended our adventures with the belief that the medical crisis, so-called, in the United States arises out of the fact that one system of medicine and/or healing arts dominates the landscape. The military-industrial complex has given way to the pharmaceutical-medical complex. It is a medical dictatorship which does much good as well as much harm. However, in a free country, a resourceful and curious person can find and practice alternatives and have some beneficial adventures in healing.

On days when I thought about it, I could feel anger toward conventional medicine and dentistry and the drug industry. Anger, however, does not support wellness. It is much better to look for the lessons of an experience than to wail about one's fate. As much as we thought we had learned, I suspected there was a deeper meaning to disease which no one fully understands. The "spider bite" was a lesson and a gift.

Spider's Song

Silk thread drops as from the sky
In the dark can sense the breath
A sleeper, dreaming, close to death
Spider bit her on the eye.

Spider nipped her on the head
Brought a gift so venomous
Filled her pretty eye with pus
Arachnid juices for the dead.

Arrow fired past the moon
Messenger of destiny
Brings her soul testimony
Of the body's certain ruin.

Spider brings anxiety
Wakens her at night in fright
Now I lay me all my might
She will pray her soul to see.

Spider kisses in the dark
Fractures bubbles of the mind
Spins symmetrical design
Keeps attention on the mark.

Spider shaped like number eight
Brings purifying poison
And before her work is done
Spins a careful web of fate.

Turning slowly in the strings
Consumed by limitations
And physical frustrations
Listen as the spider sings:
Weaving changes all the day
Weaving changes is my play
Sing my song don't hesitate
Spider tells you to create.

Let the poison kill the dread
Transform it to elixir
A fundamental mixture
Use it like a sandwich spread.
Poultice for the spider's pain
And pain is a perception
Illusory deception
Which eviscerates the gain.

Spider spit can make you live
Enlightened by the stinging
Embrace the spider's singing
Spider is a gift God gives.

Epilogue

During the final preparation of this book I contacted all of the heroes of our story to get permission to use their names. It was fun to see or talk to all of them again.

Mr. Mechem dropped by the house and double-checked us for geopathic stress and any unusual electromagnetic energies. He showed us his latest tools for measuring energies and deflecting them. He left us a current article from the *American Dowser Digest* which recaps experiments done in the Slovak Republic on the effects of geopathic areas on educational facilities. "Meech" is going strong, still learning, still investigating; helping people.

Micheline hasn't been teaching Tai Chi lately. She's been going to massage school to get a license and plans to incorporate breathing exercise into her therapy. She and her well-known artist husband have moved down from the mountain with their two school-aged kids.

Sabrina Stevens is still in Hawaii but has made a change and is developing her own line of cosmetics.

Dr. Bart Smith still practices chiropractic in Honolulu.

I have classes from Fred Epping a couple of times a week. Several of his students, including me, have gone through all five parts of wild goose Qigong and are now working on an internal form of Kung Fu. By internal, I mean that, instead of thinking about hitting people (Kung Fu is a martial art) we use the movements to try and expand our consciousness of energy. On Saturdays, in the warmer months, many of his students gather on the green in Lithia Park where we create a spectacle, in slow motion, for the tourists. Fred still plays guitar with his band most weekends.

Dr. Turska, my favorite character in the book, died in 1996.

We've seen Dr. Osterhaus often during the last three years. He's our family doctor and nutritional advisor and gives terrific adjustments. Dr. "O," as we call him now, has just moved to a new office in Medford.

Renee Scherling still does an occasional colonic, but has become very successful selling Mannatech products—providing evidence that there is justice in the world. It is always fun to visit Renee. She is a true healer and good friend to all who know her.

Diane Taudvin has an active massage practice in Ashland and has been serving as president of the board of the Community Food Store. Diane became a patient of Doug Leber after Linda did and is now an expert on cavitation surgery and biological dentistry, as well as being a great source of information on alternative health practices and practitioners.

Doug Leber is still doing investigational research with the Computron. If I were really ill and didn't know why, Doug would always be one of the first persons I would call. I have a very short list of geniuses whom I have met and Doug is very near the top.

Dr. Terry Lee called to tell me it was okay to use his name. He's still out in front, a leader in his field, still practicing in Phoenix, and is currently on the boards of four different dental associations. He wanted to make sure that I understood (he had just read my chapter titled "Cavitation Surgery") that it was the toxins of the bacteria trapped in the dentin of root-canaled teeth that caused most of the problems.

Jack Taylor, of course, is the fictitious name I used to represent the several radionics practitioners I have met or talked to by phone. I do work with a radionics practitioner as does Linda and a growing list of relatives and friends. Recently, my only root-canaled tooth (I had it done before I read the book!) abscessed over a weekend. I have never experienced such pain and sat in a chair with hot and cold packs on my jaw for two days. On Monday, I called "Jack" and left him a message telling him I intended to have it pulled. He called me back that evening and told me to hold off, that he could take care of it. In three days, the swelling subsided and I could chew on the tooth within a week.

Linda Smith—well, she's better than ever!

Reading List

Alternative Medicine: The Definitive Guide. Puyallup, Wash.: Future Medicine Publishing, Inc., 1993.

Bach, E. *Heal Thyself.* Sante Fe, N.M.: Sun Publishing Co., 1985.

Baker, E. *The Unmedical Miracle—Oxygen.* Indianola, Wash.: Drelwood Communications, 1991.

Bird, C. and P. Tompkins. *The Secret Life of Plants.* New York: Harper & Row, 1973.

Bland, J. *The Doctor's Syllabus for Advances in the Diagnosis and Treatment of the Chronically Ill Patient.* Gig Harbor, Wash.: HealthComm, Inc., 1991.

Bode, C., ed. *The Portable Thoreau.* New York: Penguin Books, 1982.

Boyle, T. Coraghessan. *The Road to Wellville.* New York: Viking Press, 1993.

Brennan, B. *Hands of Light: a Guide to Healing Through Human Field Energy.* New York: Bantam Books, 1988.

Brown, S., and M. Takahashi. *Qigong for Health.* U.S.A.: Japan Publications, Inc., 1986.

Caddy, E. *God Spoke to Me.* Scotland: Findhorn Press, 1992.

Cameron, E., and L. Pauling. *Cancer and Vitamin C.* Philadelphia: Camino Books, 1993.

Cameron, J. *The Artists' Way, a Spiritual Path to Higher Creativity.* New York: Jeremy P. Tarcher, 1992.

Capacchione, L. *Recovery of Your Inner Child.* New York: Simon & Schuster, 1991

Carter, James P., M.D. *Racketeering in Medicine.* Charlottesville, Va: Hampton Roads Publishing Co., Inc., 1993.

Cheney, M. *Tesla: Man Out of Time.* New York: Dell Publishing, 1981.

Corbett, J. *Laboratory Tests and Diagnostic Procedures with Nursing*

Coulter, H. *Homoeopathic Science and Modern Medicine.* Berkeley, Calif.: North Atlantic Books, 1981.

Coulter, H. *Homoeopathic Medicine.* St. Louis, Mo.: Fomur, Inc., 1975.

Coulter, H. *Divided Legacy: the Conflict Between Homoeopathy and the American Medical Association.* Berkeley, Calif.: North Atlantic Books, 1982.

Chronic Fatigue Syndrome. America On-Line: National Chronic Fatigue Syndrome Association, 1992.

Davies, R. *Dowsing: Ancient Origins and Modern Uses.* Great Britain: The Aquarian Press, 1991.

Deglin, J., et al. *Davis's Drug Guide for Nurses.* 2nd ed. Philadelphia, PA: F. A. Davis Company, 1991.

Donsbach, K. *Oxygen.* USA: Wholistic Publications, 1991.

Dorland's Illustrated Medical Dictionary. Philadelphia, Pa.: W. B. Saunder's Co., 1988.

Duff, K. *The Alchemy of Illness.* New York: Bell Tower, 1993.

Duffy, W. *Sugar Blues.* New York: Warner Books, 1976.

Dunne, L., and Kirschmann, J. *Nutrition Almanac.* New York: McGraw-Hill Books, 1984.

Evans, J. *Introduction to the Benefits of the Bach Flower Remedies.* Great Britain: The C.W. Daniel Company, Ltd., 1987.

Gerber, R. *Vibrational Medicine.* Sante Fe, N.M.: Bear & Co., 1988.

Graves, T. and J. Hoult, eds. *The Essential T.C. Lethbridge.* London: Routledge & Kegan Paul, 1980.

Gurudas. *Flower Essences and Vibrational Healing.* San Rafael, Calif.: Cassandra Press, 1989.

Harte, J., et al. *Toxics A to Z.* Berkeley, Calif.: University of California Press, 1991.

Holmes, G., et al. "Chronic Fatigue Syndrome: A Working Case Definition," *Annals of Internal Medicine.* 1988.

Huggins, H. *It's All in Your Head: the Link Between Mercury Amalgams and Illness.* Garden City Park, N.Y.: Avery Publishing Group Inc., 1993.

Illich, I. *Medical Nemesis: the Expropriation of Health.* New York: Random House, Inc., 1976.

Jensen, B. *Tissue Cleansing Through Bowel Management.* Escondido, Calif.: Bernard Jensen Enterprises, 1981.

Jensen, B. *Foods That Heal.* Garden City Park, N.Y.: Avery Publishing Group Inc., 1988.

Jensen, B. *Arthritis, Rheumatism and Osteoporosis.* Escondido, Calif.: Bernard Jensen Enterprises, 1986.

Kaplan, M. *Crystals and Gemstones: Windows of the Self.* Boulder, Colo.: Cassandra Press, 1987.

Kent, J. *Lectures on Homoeopathic Philosophy.* Berkeley, Calif.: North Atlantic Books, 1979.

Kissane, J., ed. *Anderson's Pathology.* 8th ed. St. Louis, Mo.: C.V. Mosby Company, 1985.

Kloss, J. *Back to Eden.* Loma Linda, Calif.: Back to Eden Books Publishing Co., 1992.

Kushi, A. *Complete Guide to Macrobiotic Cooking.* New York: Warner Books Inc., 1985.

Kushi, M. *The Macrobiotic Way.* Wayne, N.J.: Avery Publishing Group Inc., 1985.

Lappe, F. *Diet for a Small Planet.* New York: Ballantine Books, 1984.

Lethbridge, T. *The Power of the Pendulum.* Great Britain: Arkana, 1984.

Lisa, P. *The Assault on Medical Freedom.* Norfolk, Va: Hampton Roads Publishing Company, Inc., 1994.

Lonsdale, D., M.D. *Why I Left Orthodox Medicine.* Charlottesville, Va.: Hampton Roads Publishing Company, Inc., 1994.

Mann, W. *Orgone, Reich and Eros: William Reich's Theory of Life Energy.* New York: Simon & Schuster, 1973.

Meinig, G. *Root Canal Cover-up Exposed.* Ojai, Calif.: Bion Publishing, 1993.

Mermet, A. *Principles and Practice of Radiesthesia.* Great Britain: Element Books, Ltd., 1987.

Monte, T. *World Medicine: The East West Guide to Healing Your Body.* New York: Jeremy Tarcher/Perigee, 1993.

Murphy, M. *The Future of the Body.* New York: Jeremy P. Tarcher/Perigee, 1993.

Nielsen, G., and J. Polansky. *Pendulum Power*. Rochester, N.Y.: Destiny Books, 1987.

Patten, L. *Biocircuits: Amazing New Tools for Energy Health*. Tiburon, Calif: HJ Kramer Inc., 1988.

Pulley, M. *Solving the Pain Puzzle: Myofascial Pain Dysfunction Syndrome*. Dallas, Tex.: MyodData, 1990.

Physician's Desk Reference. Montvale, N.J.: Medical Economics Data Production Company, 1995.

Russell, E. *Report on Radionics*. Great Britain: The C.W. Daniel Company, Ltd., 1991.

Sams, J., and D. Carson. *Medicine Cards*. Sante Fe, N.M.: Bear & Co., 1988.

Sanford, J. *Healing and Wholeness*. New York: Paulist Press, 1977.

Schimmel, H., M.D., D.M.D., and V. Penzer, M.D., D.M.D., d. sc (hc). *Functional Medicine: Origin and Treatment of Chronic Diseases*. Germany: Carl F. Haug, 1996.

Sharaf, M. *Fury of Earth: a Biography of Wilhelm Reich*. New York: St. Martin's Press/Marek, 1983.

Sheehy, G. *The Silent Passage*. New York: Simon & Schuster, Inc., 1991.

Tansley, D. *Dimensions of Radionics*. Albuquerque, N.M.: Brotherhood of Life, Inc., 1992.

Tansley, D. *Radionic Healing: Is It for You?* Great Britain: Element Books, Ltd., 1988.

Tansley, D. *Ray Paths and Chakra Gateways: an Approach to Spiritual Psychology Through Radionics*. Great Britain: C.W. Daniel Co., Ltd., 1985.

The Biochemical Handbook. St Louis, Mo.: Formur, Inc., 1976.

Thoreau, Henry D. *The Natural History Essays*. Salt Lake City, Utah.: Peregrine Smith Books, 1980.

Trowbridge, J., and M. Walker. *The Yeast Syndrome*. New York: Bantam Books, 1986.

Weed, S. *Menopausal Years: the Wise Woman Way*. Woodstock, N.Y.: Ash Tree Publishing, 1992.

Wethered, V. *An Introduction to Medical Radiesthesia and Radionics*. Great Britain: C.W. Daniel Co. Ltd., 1974.

Wigmore, A. *The Wheatgrass Book*. Wayne, N.J.: Avery Publishing Group, Inc., 1985.

Wigmore, A. *The Sprouting Book*. Wayne, N.J.: Avery Publishing Group, Inc., 1986.